5/22

# ONE LAKELAND SUMMER

Camping on a farm in the Lake District following a successful business trip, young American Mike Carter Junior sees the farmer's daughter, Amy Palmer, for the first time and falls instantly head-over-heels in love. But Mike is due back in the States, where his fiancée Kari Reynolds is finalising the arrangements for their wedding. Then Kari travels to the Lakes to win her fiancé back. Meanwhile, Mike's arrival has set off a chain of events that could well end in tragedy . . .

*Books by Teresa Ashby
in the Linford Romance Library:*

LOVE ON ICE
FOR THE CHILDREN'S SAKE
THE CALL OF HOME
A ONE-MAN WOMAN
FOOL'S PARADISE
CHERISH THE DREAM
WITHOUT A SHADOW OF DOUBT
TAKE A CHANCE ON ME
RUTH'S WAR
CORY'S GIRLS
SHACKLED TO THE PAST
THE GIRL FROM YESTERDAY
SEEK NEW HORIZONS
ANGEL'S TEARS
DOCTOR'S DECISION

TERESA ASHBY

# ONE LAKELAND SUMMER

*Complete and Unabridged*

# LINFORD
*Leicester*

First published in Great Britain in 1994

First Linford Edition
published 2014

A catalogue record for this book is available
from the British Library.

ISBN 978–1–4448–2115–4

Published by
F. A. Thorpe (Publishing)
Anstey, Leicestershire

Set by Words & Graphics Ltd.
Anstey, Leicestershire
Printed and bound in Great Britain by
T. J. International Ltd., Padstow, Cornwall

This book is printed on acid-free paper

# 1

All was still in the meadow. Rabbits, enjoying the early-morning sun, twitched their ears and turned their heads curiously towards the small tent pitched unobtrusively beneath a copse of silver birches. From within came the sound of a yawn, long and luxurious — the kind that follows a really good night's sleep.

The tent's zipper rasped, the rabbits disappeared, and a dark tousled head poked through the opening, its owner smiling broadly at the promising morning. Mike Carter crawled from the tent, straightened up and stretched. Then he looked into the distance towards the still, silver waters of the lake and the shadowy rise of the mountains beyond, and he couldn't escape the feeling that he really had discovered heaven on earth. In his 25 years, he'd travelled widely and seen some marvellous sights, but nothing had ever given him the sense of complete tranquillity that he felt here.

Hunger pangs reminded him that he hadn't eaten since yesterday and he dived back into his tent, lightly chastising himself for his complete lack of organisation. He'd been too busy enjoying himself yesterday to stock up with groceries and fresh foods. The previous day, he'd ridden a hired bicycle for miles, from Ambleside to Keswick and back again, taking in the most breath-taking scenery along the way.

On his mind now, though, far more than lakes and mountains, were food and the memory of a farm not too far away which, according to a sign he'd passed in the lane, offered bed and breakfast. Maybe he'd be able to have breakfast and buy some provisions there. Hopeful, he hurried off across the meadow, the grass springy beneath his feet.

As Mike approached the farm, a tractor was trundling slowly along the rutted lane. He walked on, turned a corner, and was confronted by a cluster of farm buildings dominated by a big, square farmhouse. He paused and looked around, his eyes settling on a young woman who was scattering grain for the hungry hens which crowded around her feet. He hesitated for a moment, then he was moving forward again, his stride purposeful and quick.

★ ★ ★

In the conference room on the top floor of one of America's finest hotels, Kari Reynolds, a high-ranking executive, stood among a group of similarly high-powered-looking people. Elegantly dressed and stunningly attractive, Kari had all the confidence and sophistication of some-one much older. The people working for her recognised her exceptional organisa-tional abilities and respected her.

She glanced at her wrist watch. It was small, elegant and expensive. 'I don't need to spell it out to you,' she said.

'This conference is the biggest and most important we've ever handled. Security must be tight. You've all been fully briefed, but if there are any questions, I'd rather you asked them now.'

No one spoke. Her face relaxed and her radiant smile softened her features immediately. 'And thank you, everyone,' she went on. 'It's been short notice, but you've all coped fantastically. I'm proud of you.'

Then, gathering up her bag and her jacket, she turned on her heel and headed towards the lift. Outside the building, the car park attendant handed her her keys and she ran down the steps to her gleaming red Mercedes. Quickly, she joined the busy lunch-hour traffic and headed towards one of the most exclusive districts of Richmond, Virginia.

Lunch with her future father-in-law was always a special occasion. He made sure of that.

She smiled to herself and pressed her

foot a little harder on the gas. She was heading for a very up-market restaurant, a favourite venue for the rich, the famous and the would-bes. It was a cosmopolitan area seething with people from all walks of life, and it was a part of her home town that Kari loved and in which she felt really alive.

She saw him at once, an older version of Mike, with silvery lights in his dark hair and eyes only a little less blue than his son's. Michael Carter Senior was a tall, imposing figure dressed, as always, immaculately and stylishly in an expensive suit.

He rose as she approached, a broad smile telling her just how welcome she was. 'Kari! You look wonderful, honey.'

'Thanks, Dad.' She held his hands as she kissed his cheek. Although he was not yet her father-in-law officially, as far as Kari was concerned he had been 'Dad' for some time. He held out her chair while she sat down. 'I appreciate your taking time out to have lunch with me, Kari,' he said in his deep, sonorous

5

tones. 'I know how busy you are right now.'

'Never too busy to see you.' She laughed and her eyes twinkled. This man had always been part of her life. The Carters and the Reynolds went back a long way, and soon the two families would be united in marriage.

'Less than two months until the wedding of the year,' Michael joked. 'How are the preparations coming along? There must be a lot to do.'

'Tell me about it!' She groaned. 'I can't believe it's only a few weeks away. There's still so much I haven't done.'

'Oh, I'm sure with your management skills, a mere wedding will be a pushover.' He chuckled. Kari suddenly looked forlorn. It was a rare expression for her and Michael reached across the table and squeezed her hand. 'Something bugging you, Kari?'

She shrugged. 'Well, things would be easier if my bridegroom-to-be were to put in an appearance sometime soon,' she said dryly.

Michael Carter leaned back in his seat, visibly relieved. 'Is that all? He'll be back home in two or three days, full of joy and raring to go.'

Kari lifted her shoulders and her eyes shone lovingly as she thought of her fiancé. 'I'm missing him so much,' she said. 'I just can't wait to see him again.'

'I know, honey. We've missed him, too. But I guess he deserved a break after he'd wrapped up that business deal in Manchester, and what harm can he come to in a tent?'

'None, I guess.' Kari smiled.

'He negotiated really well and there's a lot of money in it for us,' Michael Senior went on proudly. 'I shouldn't be surprised, though. Once that boy's made up his mind he wants something, that's it. He goes all out to get it.'

'In fact, he's just like his father.' Kari smiled indulgently.

'Yeah! Maybe he is a chip off the old block at that,' Michael Carter chortled.

'I just wish he'd come home, that's all,' she said wistfully.

'Well you know how he is about the great outdoors, Kari. He couldn't miss out on seeing the English Lakes, not when he was so close. They say the area's really something . . . '

Kari picked absently at her napkin. She'd never have thought it possible that she could miss anyone so much. She'd always prided herself on her independence, guarding it fiercely. But, without Mike, she felt as though a part of her was missing.

'I just wish I could have gone with him,' she said softly. 'But I couldn't spare the time, what with the wedding to arrange and this oil industry conference too.'

'Well, I'm glad Mike's not here,' his father said. 'It means I can have you all to myself for a change. I know I've said this before, Kari, and I'll probably go on saying it for the rest of my life, but don't forget, you're the daughter Barbara and I never had. We love you, we're proud of you and we couldn't be happier about this marriage.'

Kari squeezed his hand in return. 'Thanks, Dad,' she said gratefully. 'You know, Mike's always been the only guy for me. I've always loved him and I always will.' Her eyes glittered possessively. 'Nothing will ever come between us, ever!'

* * *

The girl among the chickens wore faded blue jeans and a checked shirt. Her fair hair shimmered in the sunshine. As Mike approached, she looked up and smiled and it was as though he'd been hit in the face, so physical was the impact.

He was confused and bewildered, yet at the same time uplifted. There was something about this girl, something he didn't understand or recognise, something that took his breath away and made his heart pound.

It was powerful, hypnotic and totally unexpected; and before she even spoke to him, Mike understood.

It was love. Love at first sight!

He hadn't believed such a thing existed. It was crazy — ridiculous — but it couldn't be anything else.

He fought desperately to gather his wits, to think of something to say, but he had been struck dumb. 'Good morning!' the girl said, seizing the initiative, while Mike floundered helplessly in a sea of confusion. 'You're up and about early. What can we do for you?'

'Hi,' he managed to mumble at last. He'd never felt like this before, never known what it was to be unsure of himself. Just when it was crucial that he should be cool and sophisticated, he was stumbling over his words like a gauche teenager.

'I . . . uh . . . your sign says you do breakfast,' he said nervously. He thought of Kari. There had never been anyone serious in his life but Kari, never! Kari was beautiful and clever. He adored her and he'd never once cheated on her, or even wanted to. But if he had hoped that thinking of his fiancée would steady him, he was wrong. It made him feel worse, even more aware of his feelings towards this total stranger.

'Oh, you're American,' she said, holding out her hand. 'Hello, I'm Amy Palmer.'

'Hi. Mike Carter.' He shook her hand, prepared for the impact of her touch, yet still taken by surprise by the alarming increase in his pulse rate. *I must be sick*, he thought, desperately trying to find a reason for all this, any reason at all, apart from the one he'd already come up with. Her lovely smile was the most beautiful thing he'd ever seen.

'We do have several guests staying with us, but they won't be up yet,' she said. 'You'd be welcome to join my family for breakfast, though.'

'That's OK. Really. I wouldn't like to impose,' he said weakly.

'Come on in.' She smiled warmly. 'There's always more than enough for everyone.'

11

Mike sat at the table, his head still in a spin. The farmhouse kitchen was vast and traditional, with a flagged stone floor and an Aga cooker set into a huge arched alcove. The breakfast smells were mouth-watering and welcoming. And, from the moment he'd walked in, Amy's parents, her two brothers and her kid sister had made him feel like a member of the family.

He tried to think of the traditional Virginian house in a tree-lined avenue in Richmond in which he and Kari would live. Every conceivable modern convenience had already been installed and he'd thought he loved it. But, somehow, compared to this, it lacked real warmth. As for the food here — he'd never tasted anything like it. Someone else, though, had been drawn to the kitchen by the delicious aroma. The door opened and a black Labrador with a sun-rusty sheen to her coat walked in, nose raised in the air, sniffing. Her eyes fell on Mike and she immediately pegged him as a newcomer and walked sedately across to him, her tail swishing.

'Bracken!' Amy called her away.

'No, please, leave her.' Mike smiled, tickling the dog's ears, while she gazed up at him with deep brown eyes. 'When did she have her pups?' Mike directed his question at Amy.

'Oh, you noticed!' Amy laughed. 'Just a few weeks ago. Would you like to see them?'

'I sure would,' he said with genuine enthusiasm. 'I guess I've always had a soft spot for retrievers.'

Bracken began to wriggle and squirm as Mike got to his feet, almost as if she couldn't wait to show off her pups.

'Just follow her.' Amy laughed. 'She'll show you the way. But I'll come along, too, just to make absolutely sure you don't get lost.'

Bracken led the way to a hayshed where her seven black velvet pups were safely housed in a pen. She heaved herself over the low barrier and sat amongst them, looking up at Mike and Amy, almost quivering with maternal pride. Amy stood close to Mike, so close that their arms touched. He glanced at her, but she was watching the pups as they clambered and frolicked about the pen. Her whole face seemed so alive, so vital. She turned to look at him and he had to look away quickly, reluctant to meet her eyes, to give away how he felt.

The biggest of the pups waddled across to Mike right away and scrambled onto his knees. His tiny, sharp baby teeth dug into Mike's fingers.

'You'll have to watch him.' Amy giggled. 'We call him Gnasher.'

'I can see why.' Mike grinned. 'He's terrific, though, isn't he? It must be great,' he went on, 'working on a farm. A real one, I mean, where the animals can roam freely. I guess you're pretty busy at this time of year,' he added. He couldn't believe it. Here he was, angling to find a way of asking her out. And he wasn't finding it at all easy. She'd picked up one of the pups and was resting her cheek against its head. 'Do you . . . do you manage to get a break at all in the evenings?' he went on, hoping for a word, a hint, anything he could latch on to.

'Most evenings I help out at my uncle's pub, the Ram's Head, down in the village. It's pretty busy at any time but, just now, with all the tourists around, he needs all the help he can get.'

'I, uh, guess you don't get a lot of time off, then?' he went on, watching her closely.

She looked at him quizzically, her head on one side, as though she were trying to figure him out. Flustered and embarrassed, he pulled his wallet from his hip pocket. 'I must pay for my breakfast,' he said. 'And could I buy some eggs and milk, if you can spare any?' His hands shook as he opened his wallet and a photograph fell to the ground.

Amy saw it first and stooped to pick it up, pausing to look at the beautiful girl. 'She's lovely,' she commented. 'Is she someone special? Your girlfriend?'

He took the picture and looked at it steadily. 'Her name's Kari.' But saying her name didn't make him feel the way it should. 'Well, I guess she is special. She and I go back a long way. Our families have been friends for years, you know how it is.' He was being evasive, he realised. 'She's a great girl, a good friend.' He broke off and realised Amy was staring at him, smiling warmly. Suddenly, she seemed to jump and pulled back the cuff of her shirt to look at her watch.

'Crikey, look at the time! Mum'll need help getting breakfast for the guests. Come on, I'll get your eggs and milk before you go.' She hurried back into the farmhouse and emerged shortly afterward with a carrier bag. 'There.' She handed it to him. 'Any time you need anything, feel free to call by. We always have plenty of fresh dairy produce.'

Mike thanked her and turned to go, strangely reluctant to leave her. When he turned around, she was watching him. 'Thanks again,' he said, walking backwards, not wanting to let her out of his sight. He had the absurd urge to shout to the world that he was in love; to throw himself on his knees at her feet and confess to his feelings.

In the end, it was Amy who turned and walked away, leaving Mike feeling curiously empty. Empty and alone.

A little way down the track, he put down the eggs and milk and took out the photograph of Kari. She was beautiful — her lively green eyes laughed out at him and he knew that most guys would give their eye teeth to be in his position.

Then why couldn't he stop thinking about Amy? The farther away from the farm he got, the more Amy intruded upon his thoughts. And knowing he'd probably never see her again hurt more than he could have imagined. In fact, it hurt a lot more than saying goodbye to Kari had, when he'd left for his trip to England.

As his legs still ached from all the cycling of the day before, Mike was glad later on that he had his hired Land Rover to drive into the small town, which was seething with tourists. He managed to find a parking space outside the bank and loped inside, his long, slim legs taking him up the steps two at a time. He strode over to an empty position and smiled at the female teller.

'Hi,' he said cheerfully. 'Beautiful day, isn't it?'

'Good morning,' she replied coolly, obviously not impressed by his hearty approach.

'I'd like to draw out some cash,' he said as he reached into his hip pocket.

'Do you have some form of identification?' the girl queried crisply.

'I can do better than that.' He grinned and slid a letter from the bank's head office beneath the glass partition. 'You should find that in order.' Then he took a gold card from his wallet and pushed that across with the letter. The girl's

18

eyes widened as she read the letter. Then she smiled up at Mike, her cheeks flushing.

'Just a moment, sir,' she said and hurried off.

'Mr Carter?' A man in a suit quickly appeared. 'I'm Alan Ladbury, manager of this branch. I'm so sorry to keep you waiting.'

Mike grinned. The way people could always be swayed by money never ceased to amuse him. The manager insisted on serving Mike himself, making it abundantly clear that nothing was too much trouble. He was soon receiving the full VIP treatment, simply because he possessed a letter which identified him as having unlimited funds available.

'Thanks a lot, Mr Ladbury,' he said, as he filled his wallet with crisp English bank notes. 'You've been real helpful.'

Time to call Kari, he thought once he was outside. He felt strangely reluctant. He hesitated. No, she'd be waiting, expecting his call, so he couldn't put it off. Quickly, he made the call before he could change his mind.

'Darling! Hi!' Kari's voice was as clear as if she'd been standing right next to him. 'I was hoping you'd call. How are you?'

For the first time ever, he was lost for words and had to think carefully before he spoke. 'I'm fine, Kari. I can't talk long. I've no way of charging my phone. How're things with you? Did you see Dad?' he asked her cautiously.

'We had lunch,' she replied, before asking hesitantly, 'Mike, are you OK?'

'Sure,' he said unconvincingly.

'When are you coming home, honey?' she went on. 'I tell you, things are really starting to happen here and I so want you to be a part of it all.' Her voice trailed off.

He hesitated again, this time a fraction too long.

'Mike, are you still there? Are you sure you're OK? You sound — weird.'

'Just feeling homesick, I guess,' he said quickly. 'I still have some business to attend to, but I should be through in a few days. Can't say when exactly, though.'

'I can't wait until you're home, Mike!' She sounded so happy. 'Then we'll be married and together all the time. In fact, next time you decide to take off, I'm coming with you, no matter what. I've missed you so much.'

'I . . . I miss you, too,' he said. He wished with all his heart that he meant it, but he felt his words had a hollow ring. Thankfully, Kari didn't seem to notice. 'I've got to go,' he said. 'My phone's almost out of charge. I'll call you again in a couple of days.'

'All right,' Kari said softly. 'Take care, darling. Remember, I love you always!'

\* \* \*

Amy Palmer dominated Mike's thoughts all day. He knew he couldn't go home without seeing her again. He felt so guilty though, about lying to Kari. The last thing he ever wanted do was hurt her, but he simply couldn't help himself. Indeed, he was still trying to tell himself that he was just going for an evening stroll when he reached Amy's uncle's pub.

It was only when he looked at the sign that he finally admitted to himself why he had gone inside the Ram's Head. He wanted to ask Amy out.

Before he lost his nerve, he opened the door and the rich, hoppy smell of beer wafted out on the warm evening air, along with the chatter and laughter of the customers. He spotted Amy at once working behind the bar and again, Mike experienced the overwhelming feeling he'd had that morning. She was so lovely.

He ambled, as casually as possible, over to the bar and caught her eye.

'Oh, hello again.' She gave him a friendly smile and he felt suddenly gauche and incredibly happy.

'Hi,' he replied at last, but she was busy attending to other customers.

He waited until it was his turn to be

served and was ecstatic when it was Amy who came to serve him.

'What can I get you?' she asked lightly. Her question took him by surprise. He didn't drink much at all at home — just the occasional glass of wine; but, as he looked around, he realised that most people seemed to be drinking beer of one sort or another.

'How about a beer?' he asked hesitantly.

A heavily built, middle-aged man sitting at the table next to the bar prodded Mike with his finger. 'You want to try a drop of real ale,' he said, winking at Amy. 'Give him a pint of Old Peculier.'

'You don't want . . . ' Amy began, but Mike was not to be so easily put off.

'A pint of Old Peculier it is.' He laughed, glad to have been rescued by the man who was obviously a regular in the pub.

'It's very strong,' Amy warned him.

'Oh, that's OK.' Mike grinned, his confidence already growing. 'What are you having . . . um . . . ?' He turned to his newfound friend.

'Sam.' The man chuckled. 'Sam Threadwell. Mine's a half of bitter, lad, thanking you.'

Amy, shaking her head, got their drinks.

When Mike took his first swig from the glass, he was pleasantly surprised at the rich, fruity taste. Sam was watching him closely, so he took another swig from his pint before setting the glass down with a sigh of satisfaction. 'Hey, that's pretty good,' he said, and Sam raised his eyebrows.

As the evening wore on, friends of Sam's arrived and joined their circle in the corner. Mike was happy to sit with them, buying rounds of drinks and getting the occasional glimpse of Amy. As the drink dispelled his inhibitions, he wasn't so discreet about watching the lovely barmaid as she worked.

'You're quite taken with our Amy, aren't you, lad?' Sam commented.

Mike turned to look at him, a huge,

soppy grin on his face. 'I think she's kind of cute,' he said. 'A real babe, in fact.'

'Ay, well, you'll not be the only one as thinks that.' Sam chuckled. 'But she's a choosy lass, that one.'

'Choosy?' Mike repeated stupidly. His head felt twice as heavy as usual.

'She went out with a local lad for a long time,' Sam went on. 'She's not been the same since they broke up.'

'So, she hashn't — I mean, hasn't — got a boyfriend at the moment?' Mike thought his voice sounded unfamiliar, as though it wasn't his at all.

'No, she's footloose and fancy-free,' Sam confirmed with a conspiratorial wink.

It was nearing closing time. Many of the tourists had gone, leaving just a few regulars and Mike. If he was going to act, it had to be now. 'Another drink, Sam?' he asked heartily, as the older man's craggy face drifted in and out of focus. Mike got to his feet and swayed, clinging to the bar for support.

'Whoopsh!' he muttered.

'Mind how you go.' Sam chortled tipsily and swayed slightly. As he watched Mike's distinctly unsteady progress along the bar, he had the strongest feeling that the lad had never been drunk before, not this drunk anyway. He was impressed, too, though. The young American had handled the strong ale better than most.

Mike reached Amy. She was wiping glasses on a cloth and stacking them beneath the bar. She smiled at him and his heart turned over. 'Amy,' he said, concentrating hard to keep his voice steady. 'I . . . I think you're absholutely beautiful. I've never, never ever, met anyone like you before.' He broke off and frowned, trying to remember what it was he wanted to say. 'Oh, yeah, and . . . and I'd love it if you'd come out on a date with me.'

Amy smiled and nodded. 'Of course you would,' she said kindly. She'd heard it all a thousand times before.

'No! I mean it. I'd really like to . . . '

His voice trailed off, his eyes rolled and, before Amy could move, Mike had slithered to the floor, unconscious.

She rushed out from behind the bar and looked down at him, lying in a crumpled heap at her feet, the huge, soppy grin still on his face.

★ ★ ★

'Sam, how could you?' Amy protested, as the locals gathered around to examine their handiwork. 'Look at the state he's in. You should be ashamed of yourselves — all of you.'

'We were only having a bit of fun, lass,' Sam said good-naturedly. 'He seems a nice lad. Not shy about buying his round.'

'Anyone here know where he's staying?' Sam addressed his friends and they all shook their heads.

'It's all right, Sam,' Amy broke in. 'He's pitched his tent in Dad's meadow. I've got my car. I'll take him back. Could you give me a hand to get him in the car? I'll give you a lift home, too. It's on my way.'

Sam nodded eagerly. After a night like tonight, he wasn't exactly looking forward to the long haul up the hill. Amy's clapped-out old car was the only vehicle in the car park.

Together, she and Sam pushed and shoved until Mike was sprawled across the back seat. The car whined disturbingly, groaned reluctantly, then burst into life with a loud bang.

'I think I've got a hole in the exhaust,' Amy laughed as they set off with the car back-firing and roaring.

Sam sobered up pretty quickly, sitting rigid. 'Can't you go any slower, lass?' he asked cheekily.

'Slower, Sam? I'm only doing twenty-five miles an hour. She just won't go any faster up this hill. Anyway, she's doing fine, purring like a kitten.'

'A kitten with bronchitis maybe,' Sam muttered. He sighed with relief when she stopped the car outside a row of stone cottages. The car gave one last whine of protest and shuddered to a halt as Amy switched off the ignition.

Almost at once, the door of the end cottage flew open and Kate Threadwell came storming out. Sam, who was half in, half out of the car, gave a little cry of alarm. He dragged himself upright and stood beside the car, swaying slightly, towering a foot above his tiny wife. He must have weighed a good six stones more than her, but the expression on his face was one of pure terror. 'Hello, love,' he said, smiling nervously.

'Don't you 'Hello, love' me!' She jabbed him with her finger. ' 'Just popping out for half an hour', you said!' She poked him again. ' 'Just having a half with the lads,' you said!'

He'd backed up until he was leaning against the car and could go no farther. Amy tried desperately to stop herself from bursting out laughing.

'Your supper's ruined!'

'Sorry, love,' Sam said, more hopeful than apologetic.

'Now thank young Amy here for

bringing you home,' Kate demanded, as though he were a child who'd misbehaved. 'Goodness knows how you'd have managed the hill in that state.'

'Thanks for the lift, Amy,' he said sheepishly.

'Now get inside.' Kate turned and winked at Amy. 'Will you be all right, lass?' She glanced anxiously in the back of the car where Mike was sprawled across the seats.

'Oh yes, this one's harmless enough. Just an American tourist who can't hold his drink. He'll be fine.'

Amy drove off then, her car spluttering and coughing as it lumbered along the bumpy road. In the back of the car, Mike began to stir. He was sitting upright, rubbing his eyes, by the time she drew up beside his Land Rover.

'Wh-what hit me?' he slurred.

'A few pints too many,' Amy said, trying not to laugh. She got out and opened his door. 'Come on,' she said briskly. 'I'll give you a hand to get to bed.' He put his arm around her

30

shoulders and she helped him with some difficulty across the meadow to the tent. His knees were wobbly and his head was swimming.

'Just stand still for a minute.' She unzipped the flaps of the tent. 'Come on,' she said. 'You'll feel better when you're sitting down. We don't want you falling over again, do we?' She smiled.

'Again?' he murmured, as he crawled into the tent. 'Wha . . . what'd I do?'

The moon was full and bright above them and cast enough light to enable Amy to find a torch. 'There,' she said. 'Now, let's get those boots off.' She untied the laces and eased them off his feet, then she yanked off his jacket.

Mike's head was spinning again, but this time it had nothing to do with the beer. It had everything to do with the soft sweep of her hair as it touched his face, the sound of her voice, the delicate scent of her perfume . . .

'Amy,' he whispered. He was gazing at her in blatant adoration, watching her every move. She was on her knees now, straightening out his sleeping bag, helping him to crawl into it.

'You need to sleep this off,' she said softly. Then, with a wry grin, she added, 'The bad news is, you'll feel even worse in the morning.' She zipped him inside the bag and smiled down at him.

'Amy,' he said again. Just saying her name made him feel good. 'Amy, I have to tell you something.'

'Go on then,' she said patiently.

'Amy!' He clasped her wrist. 'I love you! I've loved you from the first moment I saw you this morning. I mean it, I really do. I honestly love you!'

She smiled down at him, amused, then turned off the light and crawled out of the tent. Before she left, she looked back inside. 'Goodnight Mike,' she called. 'Sleep tight.'

He raised his hand and gave a sheepish little wave, then lay in the darkness, listening to her soft footfall on the grass outside.

By the time she was in her car, Mike was sound asleep and snoring.

The morning arrived too quickly. Groaning, Mike dragged his sleeping-bag up over his head. Outside, the birds sounded as loud as a heavy metal rock group, and every chirrup sent another spasm of pain through his head.

He'd never felt so awful in all his life. Gradually, as he lay there, he managed to piece together the events of the previous day.

Amy! His first thoughts were of her and, despite his fuzzy, aching head, one thing was crystal clear. He'd meant every word he'd said to Amy. He loved her! He'd never been so sure of anything in his life and he knew now exactly what he had to do.

He fumbled his phone from his pocket. This time there was no hesitation as before. It wasn't in his nature to hurt or deceive anyone and he wanted every-thing out in the open as soon as possible.

'Kari?' he asked as the receiver was lifted. She sounded a very long way away, husky-voiced and sleepy.

'Mike? Do you realise what time it is?' It sounded like she was yawning and he realised that it was still early in the States. 'Still, this is a lovely surprise, darling. When will you be home? I'm going to start mailing the wedding invitations soon.'

'Kari, I . . . '

'Hey, guess what? I heard from Joni in Wisconsin and she says she can come to the wedding after all. Isn't that great?'

Mike took a deep breath. He despised himself at this moment, letting her go on and on like that when he was about to shatter her whole life.

'I just can't wait to have you home,' Kari was saying dreamily over the phone.

'That's just it, Kari,' Mike began awkwardly. 'I'm sorry, but I won't be coming home as scheduled.'

'Oh, Mike!' Kari cried in protest. 'Baby, you promised you wouldn't let business or anything else get in the way of our wedding arrangements.'

'That's not what I meant, Kari,' he said.

'Then what do you mean?' she demanded sharply.

'I'm talking about the wedding.'

'What about it? You've nothing to worry about. I've seen to — '

'Kari . . . ' He broke off. Somewhere inside him, he felt as though his heart was being torn out. 'I . . . I don't know how to tell you this.'

'Tell me what, Mike?' Kari's voice was low now, suspicious. 'You're not making any sense.'

'I . . . I don't think there's going to be any wedding, Kari,' he said at last. 'I'm not . . . '

The phone beeped a warning that it was about to die on him.

'Kari!' he shouted, but the connection had been broken. The call had been cut. Slowly, he lowered the phone from his ear, the full enormity of what he'd done dawning on him. With that call, he knew he'd broken Kari's heart. And all because of a girl he'd known for only 24 hours.

# 2

'Thank you. You've been most helpful.' Kari put the telephone down and stared at the wall for a moment in order to compose herself, before turning to face the other people in the room.

Both her parents and Mike's were there, watching her every move anxiously. When she turned, her green eyes were bright. 'That was Mike's hotel,' she said with a tight smile. 'Apparently he checked out several days ago and told them he had no plans to return. I guess he was pretty serious about this camping business.'

Larry Reynolds got up and went over to his daughter. 'He'll call again soon, honey,' he said consolingly, glancing at the others. 'I'm sure he will.'

They'd all come round as soon as Kari called them with the news that the wedding was off and they all seemed still to be reeling from the shock.

'Yeah, he's bound to get in touch with one of us sooner or later,' Michael Carter Senior growled. 'And when he does . . . '

'Now we can't be sure of anything yet,' Barbara Carter said hastily. Although angry and upset, her instincts to defend her son remained strong. 'In fact, the more I think about it, the more I feel sure there's been some kind of silly mistake.'

'Barbara's right.' Christine Reynolds squeezed her daughter's arm. 'Mike's not the kind of boy to act rashly.'

'Then why call Kari to say the wedding's off?' Michael Senior exploded. 'If only I could talk to him — make some kind of sense out of all of this.'

'Losing your temper won't help,' Barbara admonished him.

Kari raised her chin. She seemed to be the only one staying calm, when inside her heart was breaking.

Her perfect world had been turned on its head. Her life lay in ruins.

Her mother was quick to see the look of despair on Kari's face that went unnoticed by everyone else. She put an arm comfortingly around her daughter's shoulders. 'You know, it's just possible that you misunderstood what Mike said, or misheard him even. You did say you were cut off, didn't you?'

The others murmured in agreement and Kari forced a smile.

'Maybe you're right, Mom,' she said without much conviction. 'Perhaps there has been some kind of mistake.'

⋆  ⋆  ⋆

The crippling hangover had gone, but the burning embarrassment remained like a dark shadow to haunt and torment Mike Carter Junior. The fact remained that he'd made a complete and utter fool of himself.

After calling Kari, he'd gone into the florist's and bought the biggest bouquet he could carry and was now striding purposefully towards the Palmers' farm, clutching the flowers and rehearsing his apology to Amy Palmer in his head. He turned the now-familiar corner, half-expecting to find Amy feeding the chickens, but instead he saw her standing beside her car while one of the farm hands fiddled under the bonnet.

Again his heart thudded wildly on seeing this beautiful fair-skinned English girl, but his joy was tinged with shame at the disgraceful way he'd behaved the last time he'd seen her.

As he looked on, Amy's head disappeared under the bonnet now, too, and he heard her groan.

'Sorry, love,' the farm hand said, stepping back and looking at his blackened hands. 'It's had it! The valves, the clutch — it'd cost you a small fortune to repair it. More than the car's worth.'

'Oh, no,' Amy sighed, coming back into view, her hands as grubby as the man's. 'That's all I need.' She looked so crestfallen and miserable that Mike would have done anything to bring the sparkle back to her beautiful eyes.

'I'm ever so sorry, lass.' The farm hand shrugged. 'But that's the story, I'm afraid. Now I'd better go and get cleaned up.'

'Thanks anyway, Steve.' She smiled up at him, then caught sight of Mike watching them. 'Oh no, not you again! That's all I need!'

Mike tried to apologise, but as usual, in Amy's company, he became tongue-tied and awkward.

'What do you want this time?' she demanded crossly. 'You're too late for breakfast. Besides, I didn't think you'd surface for days after that performance in the pub last night. What were you thinking of, getting yourself into such a state? It was me who took you home and put you to bed, in case you don't remember.' She slammed the bonnet of the car down and her face blazed with angry colour as she glared first at the car, then at Mike.

'I remember,' he said softly. Grinning sheepishly, he held out the flowers. 'A peace offering,' he explained, gazing at her with huge, sad eyes that begged to be forgiven. 'I wanted to apologise for last night and I don't blame you for being mad at me. I was out of order.'

She stared at him, her forehead creased in the deepest of frowns, and pointedly ignored the flowers.

'I behaved like a complete idiot,' he went on nervously. 'Please don't look at me like that, Amy. I'm real sorry about all this, but . . . but there's something I've been wanting to ask you.' He took a deep breath and blurted out the words he'd been longing to say from the very first moment he'd set eyes on her.

'I'd . . . I'd like it if you'd agree to come out with me, Amy.'

'What?' she cried, sounding more exasperated than surprised. 'Go out with you? Certainly not. I've no intention of going out with you or anyone else for that matter. In fact, as you can see, I'm not going anywhere at all anytime soon.' She pointed accusingly at the car. 'When I think of the money I've paid out on that car, and it repays me by . . . by conking out.'

Mike made the mistake of smiling.

'It isn't funny!' She rounded on him furiously. 'It's not funny at all.'

'Sorry.' Mike wiped the smile off his face. He'd obviously caught her at the wrong time. 'Maybe I'll see you at the pub tonight?' he ventured brightly, secretly hoping that by then she'd have simmered down a little and would be more approachable.

Amy glared at him without speaking and her look implied that she had better things to do than waste her breath on him. Tentatively, he took a step forward and laid the flowers on the roof of the car, smiling bashfully as she continued to glower at him.

'I'll uh, I'll be seeing you then,' he said with forced cheerfulness, but the bounce had gone out of his step as he walked away. Still, it was tough on Amy, he thought. No wonder she was upset. Wheels had to be important in a remote place like this.

Suddenly his step lightened. The wheels of Amy's car might be stilled for ever, but the wheels in his mind were positively spinning with a brilliant idea.

\* \* \*

Mike Carter Senior breezed through the art deco revolving door and found himself in the cool, air-conditioned foyer of the hotel where Kari, his future daughter-in-law, worked. The desk clerk recognised him at once.

'Go right on up, sir,' he said cheerfully. 'Miss Reynolds is expecting you.'

All the way up in the elevator, he shifted from one foot to the other, unable to stand still. He was so mad, he hardly knew how to contain his anger.

The elevator jolted to a stop and the doors swished open. With an impatient grunt, Michael Senior stepped out into the luxuriously carpeted corridor and strode quickly towards Kari's office.

With a brief knock, he flung the door open and, on finding it empty, glanced through a glass panel to the adjoining room where it looked like a meeting was in progress with Kari in charge. She was looking as bright and pretty as ever in a tailored cream suit and, with an effort, he had to suppress the feelings of anger and outrage at his son's attitude.

Here she was keeping herself busy in a desperate attempt to keep her mind off Mike and his antics and, on the face of it at least, apparently succeeding. How he admired her.

She waved when she saw him and he watched as, calmly, she excused herself and came through the adjoining door. 'Dad, hi.' Her smile was a tonic for his bruised emotions, only heightening, rather than diminishing, his anger. 'What can I do for you?' She came over to him and warmly kissed his cheek. 'Is everything all right? You look kind of . . . '

'I'm afraid everything is not all right, Kari,' he said gruffly, taking hold of her arm. 'Can we talk? It's urgent.'

'Sure,' she said, puzzled. 'Take a seat.'

She stepped back through to the other room.

'Excuse me. David, would you mind taking over here for a few minutes, please?'

* * *

She closed the door of her office behind them and said, 'Now, what's this all about? Has it something to do with Mike?' Her face paled. 'Tell me.'

'Sit down, Kari,' he said gently.

Obediently, she sank into a chair. 'What's happened?' she whispered. 'Has something happened to Mike?'

'Oh, God, I don't know how I'm going to tell you this.' He groaned. 'You don't deserve this.'

'Don't deserve what? What's going on?'

'I've just heard from Mike,' he said, his voice measured and controlled. 'I'm sorry, Kari, I'm so sorry, but it seems you were right. He does want to call the wedding off. In fact, that's just what he's gone and done.'

Kari's face crumpled and her eyes filled with tears. 'But why? Why is he doing this to me?' she whispered at last. 'What's gone wrong? What have I done?' She looked so lost and bewildered that Michael Carter's heart went out to her. 'I can't believe that this is happening,' she was saying. 'It's like some kind of nightmare. Everything was fine up until a couple of days ago, and now this has happened.'

He went over to her and put his arms around her in a comforting embrace, hating to see her hurting like this. Her body felt stiff and unyielding. 'It's nothing you've done,' he said consolingly. 'You mustn't blame yourself.'

She looked up at him with hurt, unhappy eyes. 'Why?' she whispered again.

'Kari,' he said at last, 'I can't be sure, honey, but from what Mike said — maybe from what he didn't say . . . Oh, hell, Kari, I get the impression that he's met someone else.'

Kari's already stiff body went absolutely rigid. It was obviously the last thing on her mind.

'Someone else?' she echoed, her voice faint with disbelief. 'Mike?'

'I don't understand it any more than you do,' he said angrily. 'It doesn't make any sense. As far I can tell he hasn't even been out with this girl. If I could just get my hands on him ... ' He clenched his fists. 'I just don't know what to make of that boy.'

He looked at the girl who was to have become his daughter-in-law and his face softened with affection. 'You'll never know how sorry I am about all this, Kari.'

Then, even as he spoke, a change seemed to come over her. Where a few moments ago she had been crumpled and bewildered, she seemed now to find an inner strength. 'Don't give up on us yet, Dad,' she said, her voice trembling but determined. 'I can't just let Mike go. I won't let him go! I can't let what we've had, what we've meant to each other, just . . . just slip away.' She looked directly into Michael Carter's eyes and, while a fire burned in her own, there was ice in her voice as she said, 'I just can't sit here, waiting and wondering and not doing anything. I can't!'

★   ★   ★

Mike's heart hammered as he watched Amy move from one end of the bar to the other. He knew he was probably irritating her. Every time she looked round, there he was. But he couldn't help it if he was besotted with her.

'It's been another lovely day,' he said conversationally as she passed by, but she barely acknowledged him.

'How's Bracken?' he asked next time.

'Fine,' she answered abruptly.

'And the pups?' he called after her.

'They're fine, too,' she said without turning back.

He picked up his drink, a fresh orange juice, and carried it to the table nearest the bar. His spirits had sunk to an all-time low and it was a very gloomy-looking young man whom Sam Threadwell found sitting at his table.

'Still feeling fragile from last night, are we?' Sam chuckled.

Mike looked up and was glad to see at least one friendly face, even if he did know that it was largely due to Sam's encouragement that he'd got so drunk last night.

'It's not been my day,' Mike said glumly. 'Amy isn't speaking to me and I've had a blazing row with my father on the phone.'

'Well,' Sam said as he sat down heavily and grinned at Mike, 'I'll be nice to you, lad. How about a pint of real ale? Now that's a man's drink.'

'Forget it.' Mike grinned ruefully. 'I'm sticking to straight orange juice, thanks.'

'Can't blame me for trying,' Sam teased.

'Hello, Sam.' Amy leaned over the bar. 'What can I get you?'

'Just a half, love. I promised the wife I wouldn't be late for supper tonight.'

'I should think not, too,' Amy laughed as she served him. 'Can't give you a lift tonight, Sam. I've no car. It's packed up.'

Mike flashed his easy smile. 'No problem. I've got my car outside.' Mike beamed at her. 'I could give you a ride home tonight if you like. Kind of repay the favour.'

'That won't be necessary,' Amy replied coolly, banging Sam's drink down on the bar.

'It's no trouble,' Mike persisted. 'And I promise, no alcohol!'

'No thank you.' She said each word firmly and pointedly. 'And if that wasn't clear enough, I do not want a lift! Right?'

Sam laughed and nudged Mike as Amy moved off to the other end of the bar with her nose in the air. 'That's you put in your place.' He chortled. 'I'd say she wasn't interested, son. Told you she was choosy, didn't I?' Sam drained his half-pint and ordered another; and when Mike reminded him that he'd promised not to be late for supper, he merely shrugged. 'I'm enjoying the show too much,' he said wryly. 'You watching our Amy, her ignoring you at every opportunity. You won't take a hint, will you?'

It was shortly before closing time that Mike finally admitted to himself that he wasn't going to get anywhere with Amy, at least not this way.

Sam was still there getting pleasantly sozzled. 'You off then?' he called with some disappointment, as Mike rose from his seat.

'No point in hanging around,' Mike said dejectedly. 'Maybe you could give this to Amy for me, Sam? It's just a note.'

'Love letter, eh?' Sam said with a wink as he took the envelope. 'Well, you're a trier, I'll give you that.' He watched Mike leave and call out a goodbye to Amy as he went.

'Bye, Mike,' she said in reply, then

turned back to her customers.

Sam smiled and fingered the envelope Mike had left with him. He looked round to see Amy leaning on the bar looking down at him, her grey eyes smiling.

'Sam, you're going to be in big trouble again when you get home,' she said.

'Oh, I don't think so.' Sam's eyes twinkled with mischief.

'Why? What are you up to, Sam?'

'Me? Nothing. Here, this is for you.' He handed her the envelope. 'The American lad left it.'

She sighed and took it and Sam was pleased when she didn't move away, but stood right where she was to open it. He craned his neck, trying to see what was inside, but all that fell out was a couple of keys on a ring. 'What's this?' She picked them up and looked again inside the envelope. Attached to the key ring was a label and when Amy read it, she frowned and walked out of the bar.

Mike had parked his Land Rover a

little way from the pub, but close enough so that he could see Amy's reaction when she saw the brand-new car which was all hers. His excitement grew as the pub door opened and Amy charged outside, heading straight for the car. He wound the window down, but soon realised that her reaction was not at all what he had expected.

Sam, who had followed her outside, stood scratching his head as she stepped back, hands on hips, looking up and down the road. 'What a nerve!' she shouted angrily. 'What does he take me for? Make sure it's locked up, Sam. I'm going to find Mister Michael Carter and give him a piece of my mind.'

She stormed off, muttering to herself, while Sam gleefully checked all the car doors. This was going to be something to tell the wife. She wouldn't mind him being late at all when he told her of the goings-on in the pub tonight.

★ ★ ★

Mike drove back to his tent, trying to figure out just where he'd gone wrong. He'd bought Kari a car once and she'd been delighted.

But that had been different, a small voice at the back of his mind reminded him. It had been an engagement present.

But Amy needed a car, he told himself. And he could afford it, so why the heck not? He got back to his tent several minutes before she roared up, blazing mad, in her uncle's car.

'Hi,' he said, a little nervously.

She didn't speak right away, but flung the keys of the new car at his feet. 'Stop playing stupid games. What kind of a person do you think I am?' she yelled, not giving him the chance to explain. 'You're crazy! Did you really think I'd accept a present like that from someone I hardly know? I want you to go. Leave! Get off my father's land. Now! And don't ever come near me again. Got it?'

'Look, Amy, I'm sorry,' he said, desperate to put things right between them. 'I really didn't mean to offend you. I just can't . . . well, I can't help how I feel about you. You can send me away, but please don't expect me to forget all about you. I've already sacrificed everything for you.'

Her shoulders slumped. The anger dissipated, but she remained confused. 'Just go,' she said softly. Then, turning quickly, she stomped off.

But try as she might, she couldn't get his mysterious words out of her brain.

What on earth had he meant when he said he'd sacrificed everything for her?

★ ★ ★

With a last look around the peaceful meadow which had been home for such a short time, Mike Carter found himself crossing the Palmers' land. The rucksack slung over his shoulders was his only luggage. He walked head down, so lost in thought that he didn't hear his name being called at first. Then he looked up to see Jed Palmer, Amy's father, waving to him. The man was working alone in the field and Mike felt compelled to go over and say goodbye; to have one last memory of this enchanted place to take away with him.

'So, you're moving on?' Jed said conversationally. 'Had enough of our hospitality, eh?'

'Oh, it's not like that,' Mike reassured him quickly. 'I don't want to move on. It's more a case of having to.'

'Where're you headed?'

'No idea.' Mike shrugged vaguely. 'Guess I'll find some place.'

Amy's father seemed breathless and was perspiring, although the morning was still pleasantly cool. 'Well, we're full at the house,' he said slowly, 'but we've an old empty barn on the far side of the south meadow. You're welcome to that, though . . . ' He broke off suddenly, and as his face contorted with pain, he sank to the ground, clutching at his chest and his arm.

Without hesitation, Mike threw his

rucksack to the ground and rushed to Jed Palmer's side. He laid him flat, head to the side, and tried to make him as comfortable as possible. 'Hold on,' he said calmly as Jed lay there, ashen-faced, sweat beading his brow. 'You're going to be just fine. Just take it easy while I get some help.'

He stood up quickly and reached for his phone. But he couldn't dial out. The thing was dead. He looked around frantically and spotted a man working at the far side of the field, 'Hey,' he yelled, waving his arms. 'Over here! Can you give me a hand? This guy's sick!'

The man dropped what he was doing and began to run towards them, and it was then that Jed Palmer let out another moan and rolled over, uncon-scious.

'Ambulance, fast!' Mike yelled, feel-ing for a pulse in the side of Jed's neck.

Nothing.

Then he bent over the farmer's still body to give him mouth-to-mouth.

'Get a move on!' he yelled again as the man stood by, still uncertain of what to do. 'Call an ambulance! Get his wife!'

Mike felt for a pulse again. Still nothing. He went on with the compressions. The sweat was running in streams down his face and neck, trickling down his spine.

*Don't let him die. That lovely family will be devastated. Please don't let him die.*

He kept up the mouth-to-mouth resuscitation and chest compressions until he was sure Jed could breathe on his own, then he moved him into the recovery position and waited for the ambulance to arrive, knowing that he'd done all that he could. When he finally heard the sirens and saw the blue light flashing through the bushes, he started to shake with sheer relief. He stood by as the paramedics leapt into action.

One of the paramedics glanced up at him and gave him a thumbs-up sign and all Mike could do was smile in reply, his whole body weak with relief.

A faint summer breeze whispered through the window and caught at the slats of the Venetian blind. The room was shadowy and cool, and betrayed the brilliance of the day outside. Amy looked at her father and a tremor rippled through her body.

He looked so helpless lying there amidst all these tubes and machines. But, she noted thankfully, the machine beside his bed was bleeping reassuringly. Her dad had always been so strong, so healthy. She still couldn't quite believe that this had happened.

His hand around hers squeezed with surprising strength for a man who had actually 'died' earlier in the day. She smiled down at him and blinked back tears. The nursing staff had assured them that he was out of any immediate danger and that the heart attack itself had been relatively mild. With that welcome news, her mother had gone home for a short rest, and to see to things at home, leaving Amy to sit with him.

'Don't talk, Dad,' she hushed him when he tried to speak.

He smiled and squeezed her hand again. Tears welled up in her eyes. He would be all right. The doctor had said so, but . . .

'If it hadn't been for that young American's quick thinking, well, things could have been very different,' a nurse commented as she came in and adjusted the drip.

Amy gasped at hearing this revelation. 'What? I'd no idea.'

'Yes . . . if it hadn't been for Mike, I could have lain there for hours,' Jed said hoarsely. 'Could be six feet under by now.'

'Oh, Dad,' she said tremulously, tenderly stroking his brow, 'you mustn't talk like that.'

As the knowledge sank in that if it hadn't been for Mike Carter, her father would have died out there in the field, alone and in pain, Amy began to see

Mike in a different light.

If only she could have spoken to him before he went — thanked him for saving her dad's life . . .

She looked at her father and saw his eyes were closed again. He was sleeping but his colour was improving all the time, and the doctors and nurses who periodically checked on him smiled reassuringly and told Amy he was 'doing just fine'.

'Hello there,' a warm, familiar voice said softly from the doorway. Amy looked up and saw Mike. He was hesitant, unsure of himself, almost as if he expected her to throw something at him or yell at him to leave.

She smiled. 'Come in,' she said softly. He stepped into the room and closed the door silently behind him. 'I'm so glad you're here.'

'Are you?'

'He's going to be all right,' Amy whispered across the bed as Mike slipped into a chair. 'The doctors say it was only a mild heart attack. He was very lucky.'

'I'm real glad.' He smiled at her and saw her eyes were filled with warmth. He'd half expected to meet angry, suspicious eyes instead.

'You saved his life, you know,' Amy said gratefully, and as Mike began to demur, she went on, 'He'd be dead if it wasn't for you. I . . . I just don't know how to thank you enough . . . I'm sorry about last night,' she went on. 'I overreacted. I shouldn't have shouted at you like that, or been so high-handed as to order you off our land.'

He grinned. 'It's OK. I understand. I'm the one who should be apologising. I've been acting like a complete idiot.'

'Let's call it quits,' Amy said softly, glancing for a long moment at her father as if to reassure herself that he really was all right. Then she turned back to Mike and asked him an unexpected question, one which for a moment threw him completely off guard.

'The other night you said something about a sacrifice. That you'd sacrificed everything for me. What did you mean?'

His smile was so tender, so genuine that it took her breath away. 'Maybe,' he said, 'maybe I'll be able to tell you one day soon, but not right now.'

*   *   *

At any given time, Heathrow Airport was busy; but now, at the height of the holiday season, it was jam-packed with people. The arrival of a transatlantic flight had just added to the general crush as its passengers herded along the corridor.

One young woman stood out from everyone else. Her striking appearance, beautifully cut expensive clothes, shining immaculate hair, and strong but lovely features set her apart from the rest. She made her way elegantly to the information desk and tapped on it impatiently with perfectly French-manicured finger-nails.

When the pretty uniformed girl looked up enquiringly, she said, 'I called ahead about hiring a car. I understand that I have to collect the keys from here?'

'What name is the car booked under?' the girl asked pleasantly.

'Reynolds,' the young woman replied briskly. 'Kari Reynolds.'

# 3

Jed Palmer sat in a chair beside his newly made hospital bed, eyes flitting nervously from the door to the clock on the wall. He was really looking forward to going home to his family and his farm after more than a week in this room off the main ward.

At last, familiar footsteps echoed along the corridor outside and he smiled. His wife Sheila was the first to appear, with Amy right behind her. Amy's sister, 13-year-old Joanna, was in such a hurry to see her father that she actually ran past the door to his room. However, her delight at being reunited with him chased her embarrassment away.

'Dad!' she cried, rushing in to hug him.

'Go easy with your father. Remember he's not well,' Sheila Palmer admonished. But her voice was warm. 'Hello, love. All ready?'

She bent to kiss her husband and he reached up in a sudden rush of love and kissed her tenderly on the mouth. 'You know, love,' he spoke at last, 'this little brush with death has certainly made me think. Now I know just how lucky I am to have you all,' he said softly.

Amy saw the look that passed between them and her eyes filled with tears of happiness. They still loved each other after nearly 30 years of marriage.

Jed turned to look proudly at his daughters. 'And, to my amazement,' he said, smiling, 'I've even missed you two. It'll be grand to get home.'

'It must be the drugs,' Joanna joked. 'He's delirious.'

'Ah, you're here.' The ward sister came in then. 'You've come to take him off our hands, have you? Well, I'll be glad to see the back of this one, I can tell you.' She feigned a stern expression. 'He talks about nothing except his bloomin' livestock. Up until yesterday, I thought that Hilda was his wife, not a Jersey cow.'

Jed grinned sheepishly and pressed a huge box of chocolates into her hand. The sister thanked him and held out a package to Sheila. 'Fair exchange. Here's something for you — your husband's medication. It'll tide him over until his GP calls in to see him.'

Then as Sheila thanked her, her face broke into a smile and she ushered them out of the ward. 'Remember to take things easy for a while, Mr Palmer. All the best and no offence, but I don't want to see you here again.'

★ ★ ★

Back home, Jed settled himself in an armchair in the kitchen. Bracken the Labrador, delighted to see her master but sensing that he needed to be treated gently, rested her head against his knee and let him stroke her fondly.

'Oh no you don't,' Sheila said. 'It's no good getting yourself too comfortable, Jed. You're going to bed for a rest. Come on, up you get.'

'But I feel fine,' Jed protested. 'I don't need any more rest. I'm rarin' to go. I've spent the past . . . '

'Jed Palmer, you'll do as you're told,' Sheila said in her best no-nonsense voice. 'Bed! Now!' She opened the door to a little room just off the kitchen which had previously been used for storage, but which, during his stay in hospital, her two sons had converted into a bedsit.

'I just wanted to have a look at the herd, Sheila,' Jed pleaded. 'And I wanted to check on that new fertiliser and . . . '

'Leave it all to the boys,' Sheila said brightly. 'You've two strapping sons to do the work. They've got everything under control. They'll be in to see you soon, by the way. Anyway, your cows didn't even notice that you'd gone and everything is growing fine without your help. In fact, the only bad news is that you're not as indispensable as you thought you were.'

Muttering under his breath, Jed went

to take a look at his 'new' room and nodded approvingly. Joanna had arranged some meadow flowers in a vase and the bed was positioned so that he could see out into the yard.

A few minutes later, he was sitting up in bed flicking through a copy of a farming journal, resigned to his fate.

'I'll make you a cup of tea,' Sheila said sweetly; and when she returned with it ten minutes later, he was sound asleep. She picked up his magazine from the floor and put it on the bedside table, then paused to look at him for a moment. 'Raring to go, eh?' she murmured, smiling fondly.

Back in the kitchen, Joanna was on her way out with a big flask of tea and some sandwiches for her two older brothers, Ben and Craig.

'Sit down for five minutes, Mum,' Amy said, pouring another cup of tea. 'You look bushed. It's not just Dad who should be taking it easy. How's he feeling now? Still protesting?'

Sheila sat down, slipped off her shoes

and wriggled her toes.

'He's fine. He's having forty winks, I'm pleased to say.'

'It's not going to be easy keeping him from overdoing it.' Amy pulled a wry face.

'You're telling me. It's been an odd few days,' Sheila murmured. 'And all this worry with your dad has made me neglect the rest of you.' Amy started to protest, but her mother went on, 'You've had something on your mind, I know, love. I noticed something was wrong before your dad was taken ill. So what is it, Amy? Do you feel like talking about it?'

Amy's face flushed with relief. She had been bottling things up, not wanting to over-burden her mother needlessly. But now she really felt that she needed to air her feelings. 'It's Mike,' she said at last.

'Ah.' Sheila leaned back in her chair and nodded knowingly, as though she'd worked everything out long since. 'Mike.'

'He thinks he's in love with me.'

'I noticed that he was taken with you that first day he came for breakfast.' Sheila nodded, smiling. 'He couldn't take his eyes off you.'

Amy blushed. 'Mum, if it wasn't for him, Dad would have died. And now I don't know whether I really do like him, or whether I'm just feeling like this because he saved Dad's life.'

'Perhaps you need to see him again to find out,' Sheila said softly. 'It could just be history repeating itself, of course,' she added mysteriously.

Amy looked at her curiously. 'I've never told you this, love,' she began quietly, 'but I was a rather naïve young girl when I fell in love with your dad. He was older and he was practically engaged to another girl when we met, but something just clicked between us.' Her eyes were dreamy as she spoke, remembering. 'At first we tried to deny our feelings, but it was hopeless and so we started meeting secretly. Deep down, we knew what we were doing wasn't fair, but we were so much in love, we had to be honest . . . So when your dad finished with his girlfriend, she was quite naturally heartbroken. People talked, you know; said our romance was a whim, a last fling for him. Everyone fully expected him to 'come to his senses'. But I'm glad he didn't.' Sheila laughed softly. 'There was so much trouble, it would have probably been simpler to stop seeing each other; but by then, I loved him too much to give him up. We faced the storm of disapproval together and, if anything, it strengthened our love.'

Amy had never heard her mother talk so frankly before. Her throat felt tight as Sheila spoke again quietly. 'I've never regretted marrying your father, but I know I'd have regretted it bitterly if I'd let him go.' She fell silent for a moment, then poured more tea. She wasn't quite sure what she was trying to get across to her daughter, except that she wanted her to experience the same depth of love and happiness. The decision, in the end, was Amy's. 'It's uncanny, though, that Mike should turn up just when we needed him. If he hadn't felt the way he does about you, he'd never have been crossing the fields when he was — he'd probably be back in the States. Anyway, we both know what would have happened. Listen to your heart, lass. That's all you need do. That's all you can do. And for what it's worth,' she added with a bright smile, 'I like him.'

Amy blushed. 'I like him too. But all this has happened so fast. I mean, I hardly know him.'

'Well, he's obviously knocked out by you, Amy,' Sheila said. 'I mean, fancy going out and buying you a car, just like that!' She snapped her fingers. 'The whole village is buzzing with the story. Talking of the car, what became of it anyway?'

'It's still in the pub car park, where Mike left it,' Amy said. 'I wish he hadn't bought it for me. It was so extravagant. I actually accused him of trying to buy me.'

'Oh, Amy, the lad meant well. Money's obviously no object there. I'm sure it never crossed his mind that you'd react badly. You know something else? He reminds me of your dad in so many ways. He has the same qualities — a kind heart, a quick mind, and good looks. The only difference is that he's filthy rich. What more can a girl want?' she added mischievously.

'Money isn't everything.' Amy grinned wryly.

'But it doesn't have to be a point against someone either.'

Amy considered this thoughtfully. Perhaps her mother was right. Maybe she was looking for problems when there weren't any.

'Now, I'm going to have another look at your father.' Sighing, Sheila got to her feet. She padded barefoot across the kitchen and crept into the room where Jed lay sleeping like a baby.

Amy got up from the table and carried the empty cups to the sink. A knock at the door made her jump. She crossed the kitchen to answer it and her breath caught in her throat when she saw Mike standing there, his tall, rangy frame filling the doorway. 'Hi!' He smiled.

It took a moment for her to respond. Why did his smile set her heart hammering? Surely this reaction wasn't born of gratitude? 'Come in.' She stepped back and he followed her into the kitchen.

'I just called by to see how your dad's doing,' he explained a little nervously.

'Well, he . . . ' Amy began, but a commotion from the back room drowned out her reply. Mike's face broke into a broad grin as Jed's shouts became clear.

'That's young Mike! I can hear him. Come on through, lad!'

'I think you'd better go in before he has another heart attack.' Amy smiled wryly at her mother as she came out of Jed's room.

'He's in there,' Sheila said cheerfully. 'As you'll probably have gathered. Would you like some coffee, Mike?'

'Sounds great,' Mike replied. Then, with a sheepish grin of apology to Amy and her mother, he went into the back room and, at Jed's insistence, closed the door behind him.

'Sit, down, lad,' Jed said, patting the chair at his bedside. 'I'm glad you called round. I wanted to thank you personally for what you did. But for you I'd have been a goner.'

Mike sat down in the wicker chair beside Jed's bed and stretched his long legs out in front of him. The farmer's face was a healthy colour and his eyes were bright. Mike brushed aside Jed's thanks. 'I only did what anyone else would have done. Anyway, I just came by to see how you were. You're looking a heck of a lot better than you were last time I saw you.'

'And feeling it, too.' Jed lowered his voice. 'But you know what women are like. They insist on treating me as though I'm an invalid. Anyway, how come you're still around these parts? I thought you were moving on.'

'Yeah, well, I tried to book into a hotel, but everywhere's packed solid, so I'm back to camping in your field. Besides, there are other reasons for my wanting to hang around.'

'Not my elder daughter, by any chance?' Jed guessed and Mike looked up, surprised. 'I'd have to be blind not to notice,' he went on. 'She's a lovely girl, my lass, and I'd hate to see her hurt.' There was the faintest warning note in his voice. He'd never stand for any man riding roughshod over his daughter's feelings again.

'Oh, I'd never hurt her,' Mike assured him. 'I think too much of her ever to do that.'

Jed nodded. 'So you're pretty serious about our Amy, are you?'

'Yes, sir, I am. I guess I'm just looking for your approval of . . . of me.' He shrugged.

'Well, you know you have that.' Jed grinned. 'I like you and so does Sheila. But it's up to our Amy to decide. I wouldn't want to try to influence her.'

'No, no, sir. I wouldn't want you to. I really seem to have gotten off on the wrong foot with her,' Mike said ruefully.

'Give her time,' Jed said softly. 'I don't know if you know it, but she's been hurt not so long ago. It wouldn't do to jump the gun.'

Mike nodded. 'I heard someone had let her down badly.' For Amy, he'd be willing to wait forever.

'So, what are you planning to do now?' Jed said cheerfully.

'Well, I'll be going back to the States first. There are things I have to sort out back home.' He looked thoughtful for a moment, his dark eyes troubled. 'But I'll be back, you can count on that. I'm not giving up on Amy that easily.'

'You know,' Jed pondered. 'You remind me of myself and Amy's mum.'

* * *

The door opened and as Amy backed in with a tray, she caught her father and

78

Mike staring thoughtfully at her and she had the distinct feeling that they'd been talking about her.

Mike got to his feet, took the tray from her and set it down on small table.

'Thanks.' Their eyes met and he felt that all-too-familiar thrill, but for once, it wasn't Amy who turned away abruptly, but Mike who broke the eye contact.

'So, when are you going back to America?' Jed asked, picking up the threads of their conversation.

'As soon as I can arrange it. The vacation's over, I guess.'

Passing a cup to her father Amy froze at Mike's words. So he was going back so soon. And why was her heart sinking at the prospect of not seeing him again? From where she stood she could see the back of his head. She looked at his dark hair curling against his strong, tanned neck and felt a sudden thrill.

In her determination not to like him, she'd been cool with him because she was wary of falling in love with him and then perhaps losing him.

Now she couldn't bear the thought of him going back to America.

★　★　★

Mike Carter whistled jauntily as he walked back into town. Amy had been different today — friendlier, softer. Each time he met her he got the feeling she liked him a little more. Or was that just wishful thinking?

He still felt bad about Kari, of course, but he reckoned it was better to have found out now than later. He would have to make the folks back home understand, too. Right now they were hurt and upset, but once they realised he wasn't acting on a whim, they'd be sure to support him.

He was still pondering over his problems when he bumped into his erstwhile drinking companion Sam Threadwell, who was making his way up the hill towards his cottage.

'There y'are, lad,' Sam said. 'There's

a couple of blokes looking for you. They're down at the Ram's Head.'

'Thanks, Sam.' Mike quickened his pace, wondering who these guys could be and what they wanted. 'I'll buy you a drink later.'

'I'll hold you to that,' Sam shouted back and went on his way.

Turning the corner, Mike saw the car he'd bought for Amy in the Ram's Head car park and the two guys who were hanging around it. He'd forgotten all about the car.

The older of the two men wore a loud checked jacket and beige trousers and had a cigar clamped between his teeth. Mike recognised him as Joe Chilver, the guy who'd sold him the car. He went over to them.

'There you are, Mr Carter,' Joe Chilver said.

'We've been looking for you, mate,' the younger man in the T-shirt added menacingly. The older man looked embarrassed and glared at him.

'I'll do the talking, Tony. This is my

nephew Tony, Mr Carter. He's learning the business,' he added. 'He can be a little over-enthusiastic.'

Then lowering his voice, he took the cigar from his mouth and pointed it at the car. 'Lovely motor,' he said, patting the car affectionately. 'Expensive model. Very much in demand.'

'Very much in demand,' Tony repeated.

Joe Chilver cleared his throat. 'Now it's not for me to say, son, but wouldn't you be better with something more modest? Something to suit your pocket?'

'I don't get it,' Mike said, looking confused. 'I wish you'd tell me what's going on.'

'Well, look, son.' Joe draped his arm across Mike's shoulders. 'I know it's tough, you being in a strange country and all that but, well, it's like this . . . '

The two men exchanged glances. Joe Chilver dropped his cigar butt on the pavement and ground it out with his heel.

'Your payment bounced,' he said softly, looking around. 'It seems you're a bit short of funds.'

They both looked surprised when Mike burst out laughing. 'There's obviously been some mistake,' he explained. 'I've more than enough money to cover the cost of the car.'

'Course you have,' Joe Chilver said patiently. 'But you'll understand if we take the car back, just until you get things sorted out?'

'Sure, it's not your fault. Here.' Mike delved into his pocket and pulled out the keys. 'I'm sorry about this,' he said. 'I'll have a word with the bank and get back to you.'

'No hard feelings, then?' Joe Chilver unlocked the car and got behind the wheel.

Mike watched Joe drive the car away, then he turned and headed in the direction of the bank. All this was so embarrassing.

The bank was empty. He strode over to the same teller who'd served him before.

'Oh.' The girl looked up and she

didn't look pleased to see him. 'It's you.'

'I'd like to see the manager, please,' Mike said.

'Of course,' she said quickly. 'He wants to see you, too, as it happens. I won't be a moment.'

Mike was taken aback. Maybe the manager had realised his bank's error and wanted to apologise.

He looked around. His presence seemed to have created some interest within the hank. Word must have got around. Passing employees were looking at him and it made him feel distinctly uncomfortable. The sooner all this was sorted out, the better.

'Would you care to come through to my office, Mr Carter?' The bank manager, looking serious, appeared at a side door and led Mike to a small office where he invited him to sit down.

The manager stared at his computer screen, then looked at Mike, unsmiling. Mike couldn't hold back any longer. 'Look, what exactly is going on? You refused to honour a payment I made and I want to know why,' he began angrily. 'It's not good enough. Nothing like this has ever happened to me before. I demand an explanation.'

The manager looked up. 'Oh, that's quite simple. Your credit facilities have been cancelled — totally.'

'What?'

'I've received instructions direct from the United States to withdraw all your credit facilities. As from now you have no funds available in this bank. The account has been closed. I have also been asked to pass this to you.'

He handed Mike an envelope. Confused, Mike ripped the envelope open. All it contained was a brief, terse note from his father. His mouth felt dry. There was no 'Dear Mike.' Just an ultimatum.

*Come home and sort out this mess immediately! Access to all your accounts will be restored as soon as you arrive home.*

Mike glanced up at the manager. He

was sitting on the other side of the desk, his hands clasped together in front of him, his eyes sympathetic. Mike delved in his pocket and spread out his credit cards. The manager looked at them all in turn. 'What about these?'

'I'm sorry,' he said again. 'As I've already said, they're worthless.'

'I don't get it,' Mike murmured. 'I have to call my father right now.'

The manager's features softened slightly as he stood up. 'I'm very sorry, but there's absolutely nothing I can do to help. You're not a resident in this country and you don't have a job; therefore I can't even offer you an overdraft facility.'

'Yeah,' Mike said, getting up and going towards the door. 'It's OK. It's not your fault. I understand.'

But he didn't. He couldn't understand why his father had cut off his money supply. He wasn't a kid. And, besides, he'd darned well earned it.

Outside the bank, he felt in his pockets and counted up the change. He had just over ten pounds, and that was all he had in the world.

He'd never been broke before in his life. This was a new and daunting experience for him. If his father thought that he could force him into line this way, then he was mistaken. Mike's anger mounted. There was no way he'd get in touch with his father after all this, no way!

★ ★ ★

Mike leaned on the bar, waiting to be served. He glanced over at the corner table and smiled. For a change Amy was a customer in the Ram's Head. She looked fresh and lovely in a white cotton shirt and a long, swirling floral skirt, and she was with him. He could still hardly believe it.

With his last ten pounds burning a hole in his pocket, Mike had called in at the farm for Amy. He'd half expected a curt rebuff, but she'd invited him in, smiled warmly and said, 'Just let me get out of these jeans and I'll be right with you.'

Those words had been music to his ears.

He came back to the table with their round of drinks and she smiled up at him so that his heart thudded madly inside him. That smile said so much; all he wanted to know. The wariness had gone from her eyes. If it hadn't been for what had happened in the bank earlier in the day, his happiness would have been complete. Amy was so different tonight. She talked, she laughed, and she was unafraid to meet his eyes. Her eyes were beautiful. He gazed into them and was lost in their tranquillity and contentment.

Even with no money, how could he be miserable today? The occasional light touch of her hand on his arm when he made her laugh, the time that she laughed and rested her head for a moment on his shoulder, the very closeness of her, made it all wonderful.

But it hadn't stopped her from

noticing he was disturbed about something. 'Mike,' she said softly, leaning closer. 'Tell me what's wrong? Something's bothering you, I know.'

'I think,' he said gently, reaching down for her hand, 'it's time we had a talk.'

She looked concerned. 'What is it, Mike? Can I do anything to help?'

'Let's go for a walk,' he suggested.

Outside he found he was still holding her hand, and she did nothing to discourage him. They walked on in silence until they reached the edge of the lake. The water was like a mirror, reflecting the moon and the mountains. A balmy summer breeze rustled through the trees. Somewhere an owl hooted. It was beautiful, idyllic, and made what he had to say all the more difficult.

'I'm broke, Amy. All my credit's been withdrawn. I don't have a single, solitary cent. Your new car's been repossessed and my cell phone account has been cancelled. I'm so sorry. In fact, all I have is this.' He reached into his wallet and pulled out an airline ticket. 'It's my return ticket,' he said softly, staring at it as if willing it to provide him with some answers to his many questions.

Amy was suddenly fearful that he would use the ticket and vanish from her life as suddenly as he'd appeared. Unconsciously, she tightened her hold on his hand as she gazed up at him. Slowly, he turned his head to look at her.

'Are you going to use it?' she asked, her voice barely more than a whisper.

'That all depends on you, Amy,' he replied. 'Do you want me to stay?'

'I . . . ' she began awkwardly, wary of admitting her feelings, but at the same time too frightened not to. 'I don't want you to go.' Her shy, hesitant words carried the message he'd been longing to hear. Tenderly, he pulled her into his arms. She was so close, he could feel every beat of her heart.

To him she felt small and soft and vulnerable, wrapped within his embrace; and as he lowered his head, the faint,

intoxicating smell of her delicate perfume wafting around him, filling his senses
with longing.

He had waited so long for this
moment. He wanted to savour it.

Her lips were soft and sweet and as
he kissed her, he felt her fingers in his
hair.

'I love you,' he murmured against her
hair. 'You're everything I want . . . '
Then, laughing with sheer joy, he said
over and over, 'I love you! I love you!'
As she made to reply, he kissed her
again and again, lingeringly and lovingly.

When they drew apart, he held her
hands and looked deep into her eyes,
loving her so much that he didn't want
to part from her, ever.

'Mike,' she whispered, 'what did you
mean when you said you'd made
sacrifices for me? I like you, you know
that, but there's so little that we know
about each other.'

He nodded, realising she deserved
the truth — all of it. 'OK. I know it's

high time I told you everything.'

But the words suddenly died in his throat. His mouth went dry as he looked over her head at the road leading to the village. His eyes widened with shock and his heart began to pound uncontrollably. And this time it wasn't love that was the cause.

The dark-haired, beautiful girl heading towards them was none other than his fiancée.

This wasn't how he had wanted it to be. Amy didn't deserve this and he would have done anything to protect her from all the unpleasantness that was sure to come.

But he could do nothing. He was powerless.

Grimly, he said, 'I've a feeling you're about to find it all out the hard way.'

# 4

Mike waited until Jed had gone back inside the farm house after a brief chat before renewing his search for Amy. She might be determined to avoid him, but he was equally determined to talk to her.

He didn't have to look far. She was in the barn playing with the Labrador pups while their mother, Bracken, looked on. Bracken looked up as Mike walked in and her thick tail thumped on the floor, but Amy was too engrossed with the pups to notice him. Bracken was delighted to see Mike again and waddled over to him, tail swishing enthusiastically.

He bent down and stroked her head, but when she realised that he wasn't really in playful mood, she took herself out into the yard.

Amy trailed a piece of straw across the ground for the pups to chase.

Already they were showing their own distinct personalities. One was shy, another bouncy and boisterous, a third teasing and playful. As Mike looked on, he thought tenderly how lovely she looked, and the sound of her voice as she spoke to the puppies was soothing and gentle. Looking at her, he felt fit to burst with sheer love for her.

'Ow!' Amy cried as sharp little teeth sunk into her hand. 'You're a little menace!' she scolded the pup mildly. Then, suddenly, the one who had earned himself the nickname Rambo caught sight of Mike and bounded friskily towards him.

Mike's eyes were still on Amy and she suddenly seemed to stiffen before turning to look up at him. He wasn't sure what he expected to see in her eyes — anger, suspicion, pain perhaps — but having caught her off-guard, he saw only the unmistakable look of love.

He tried to speak, but the words wouldn't come. Oblivious to the puppies cavorting and tumbling about his feet, Mike tried instead to convey with his eyes what he felt in his heart. Amy's eyes widened as she looked up at him, the attraction she felt for him hitting her hard. Slowly, she got to her feet and stood looking up at him.

'Amy,' he said, his voice faltering. 'Amy, I . . . '

'It's all right, Mike,' she whispered softly as they moved together. 'It's all right.'

Words were lost as his lips touched hers. Tenderly, he held her close, caressing her soft hair. All the pain inside her vanished as she responded to his kisses, and the tears she shed were tears of happiness.

'I'm so sorry, Amy,' Mike said huskily as they broke apart. 'I wouldn't hurt you for the world. I love you so much.'

'I should have let you explain,' she butted in. 'It wasn't your fault.'

'But I think that it was. I . . . '

'No.' She placed her fingers gently over his lips. 'I should have trusted you, Mike.'

'When I've given you every reason not to trust me?' he murmured.

'I forgive you.' She smiled and kissed him, showing she'd probably forgive him anything.

Mike felt something tugging at his foot and looked down to see Rambo demolishing his boot-laces. Laughing, Amy lifted him up and gave him a quick cuddle before setting him down in the pen with the other pups. She looked so fresh and lovely, eyes shining with love and joy, face flushed with happiness; a real English rose, he thought blithely.

'We have to talk,' Amy said at last with a sigh, stepping out of the pen.

'Yeah, I know.'

'Is . . . is that girl what all the mystery's been about?' Amy asked, uncertainly. 'Was she the one you meant when you talked about sacrificing everything for me?' She looked at him, eyes dark and serious now; and when he didn't answer right away, she rushed on. 'She's so beautiful, Mike

. . . so elegant and sophisticated. I can't compete with her. She has everything. She's the type of girl you need . . . and deserve.'

'That's crazy talk, Amy!' He laughed disbelievingly. 'You're the one I love; it's you who's special. I'm really fond of Kari, but what I feel for you is in a different league.'

Amy was looking at him so trustingly, so earnestly.

'Maybe it looks as if I've given up a lot to be with you, but I've no regrets. Not even about hurting Kari, I'm almost ashamed to say. I've loved you from the first moment I saw you. It sounds corny, I know, but it's true. You're all I need or want. Now or ever.'

Amy looked away, trying to take in what he'd said. Absently, she looked towards the pen where the pups were now cuddled together, sleeping soundly. Rambo slept apart from the rest, his sturdy little body twitching spasmodically as he dreamed.

'So where do we go from here,

Mike?' she said suddenly, turning back to look at him. 'What's going to happen to us?'

'I know what I'd like to happen.' He smiled. 'I'd like us to get married.'

'Married?' She looked shocked, but her face flushed with pleasure, too. 'Oh, Mike, we hardly know each other. Marriage is, well, such a big step, and when I marry I want it to last for ever. I want to be really sure.'

'But I love you.' His eyes shone. 'Surely that's enough.'

Amy's head began to spin. She wasn't ready for all this. She couldn't take in properly what he was saying. This boy she hardly knew was asking her to marry him and against all her naturally cautious instincts, she wanted to say 'yes'. She felt so confused. Half of her was on top of the world, and the other half was trying desperately to be sensible and rational and remember that he was practically a stranger. What if Mike suddenly realised he'd made a mistake? Then she'd be left with a broken heart, and she couldn't bear that to happen again.

She took a deep breath, composed herself and said, more brightly than she felt, 'Have you considered what you'll do for money and where you'll live?'

'All I know right now is that I want to stay here, Amy — to be with you. But I've no money and nothing left in the world except my return ticket back to the States, which I don't ever intend to use. I know I'm going to have to find a job and a place to stay, but I promise we'll get through this together some-how. As long as we have each other, I know we'll make it.' He smiled reassuringly.

★  ★  ★

'How are you feeling, love?' Sheila Palmer said to her husband, Jed, when he returned to the kitchen. 'Did you enjoy your stroll around the yard?' She had to suppress the urge to rush over and help him to a chair. 'We don't want you rushing things now.' She broke off, realising he wasn't listening. In fact, he seemed quite preoccupied.

'I've just been talking to Mike out there.' He waved his hand vaguely towards the yard and chuckled. 'You'll never believe what he's just told me. He says he wants to marry our Amy. Marry our elder daughter, and we hardly know him!'

Sheila straightened up and placed her hands on her hips, chuckling at the look of bewilderment on her husband's rugged face. 'Come on, Jed. Did you think I hadn't noticed? I'm not in the least surprised.' She smiled knowingly. 'A mother senses these things, you know.'

Jed looked troubled. 'You sound so calm about it all,' he said slowly. 'He's just here on holiday, remember? We don't know what he does for a living, where he hails from — apart from the fact he's American — or who his family are. We know nothing about him.'

'Not yet, love. Not yet, but we will.'

Sheila smiled. 'Just be patient. Right now it's only the way they feel about each other that's important to them.'

'But we can't just let them get married,' Jed protested. 'He tells me that he has no money, no prospects . . . he doesn't even have a place to live apart from that tent of his. They can't exist on thin air.'

'Well, you could offer him work for a start, Jed,' Sheila pointed out. 'There's always plenty needs doing on the farm, especially with the harvest coming up. And we have a spare room he'd be welcome to.'

Jed let out a little sigh of irritation. Sheila seemed to be so taken with Mike that she was blind to the possible problems. And he wanted the very best for his daughter.

'Think about it, Sheila. He's obviously from a wealthy family. He's intelligent, well-bred. He's a nice lad, but I doubt if he's ever done any hard, physical work in his life.'

'He can learn, Jed,' Sheila said

practically. 'I know it's all happened so quickly, but don't you think Amy deserves this chance of happiness after all she's been through?'

He looked at his wife before replying. 'All right, all right, maybe we should see Mike and have a proper talk with him and Amy. Sort one or two things out.'

'I think that's a great idea, love.' Sheila smiled and took his arm. 'And I also think it would be a good idea if you had a rest.'

★　★　★

A tense Kari Reynolds leaned back against the padded headboard of her hotel bed and tried to relax. It was good to hear her mother's voice calling from the States. She didn't feel quite so alone.

'Yes, I found him OK, Mom,' she reported. 'That was the easy part. But he's really fallen for this English girl. So far, I only know her name: Amy Palmer.

We didn't get around to conversation when we met.' Kari shuddered at the memory of their meeting when she'd found Amy in Mike's arms. 'Anyway, I'm going to find out all I can about her. I'll keep you posted, Mom. And don't worry about me. I'm fine.'

'Just be careful, honey, and look after yourself.' Christine Reynolds sounded near to tears. 'I just wish you'd let Daddy and me come over with you.'

'No, I'm fine, really. I've got to sort this one out for myself. I'm just grateful that you and Daddy have been so supportive.'

'Oh, sweetheart, it must be awful for you. But if you need anything, just let us know. By the way, Daddy spoke to your boss and he says you're to take all the time you need, Kari. So don't worry about your job.'

'Mom, stop fretting. I'm OK. I've managed to get a room in a fairly decent hotel. As a matter of fact, I was really lucky to get it with it being the height of the tourist season here. Take care of yourself and love to Daddy, too. Bye, Mom.'

'Bye, darling. Good luck.'

Kari hung up and jumped off the bed. After a shower and a change of clothes, she was ready to put the second stage of her plan into action.

* * *

The residents' lounge was deserted. It seemed that everyone else was out somewhere, and that suited Kari perfectly. She ordered a drink, then settled back in her chair. When the waiter returned, carrying her drink on a tray, she seized the opportunity she'd been waiting for.

'Excuse me. I don't suppose you know a local girl called Amy Palmer, do you?'

'Amy? Yes, of course. Friend of yours?' He beamed. 'Everyone around here knows Amy. She's a lovely girl. As a matter of fact, her father supplies all the dairy produce for this hotel, but you'll know about the farm?'

Kari smiled noncommitally. 'You don't happen to know where I'd find her, do you?'

'Let's see.' He straightened up and stroked his chin thoughtfully. 'It's Friday, so Amy will almost certainly be in her uncle's pub. She helps out behind the bar in the evenings. It's the Ram's Head at the bottom of the hill. You can't miss it. Nice place, friendly, and there's always a good crowd in on a Friday night, especially in summer. You'll find her there, I'm sure.'

Kari's lips curved slightly upwards and her eyes glittered. 'Thank you very much. You've been most helpful.'

The waiter smiled nervously and moved off with the tray, only half-convinced he'd imagined the menace in Kari Reynolds' tone.

★ ★ ★

In the Palmer household, the big farmhouse kitchen was the gathering place for family conferences. Jed Palmer sat at the head of the table with his wife beside him. Amy and Mike sat together opposite. They'd drunk endless cups of coffee and Jed was quite satisfied at how well things had gone. Mike hadn't seemed to resent his many questions. In fact, the young American had seemed only too eager to talk about his and Amy's plans.

Amy had held on tightly to Mike's hand as he'd told them about Kari and the broken engagement and the way his family had virtually cut him off since he'd told them the wedding was off. He added that even though he and Amy were pretty sure of their feelings for each other, he didn't want to rush her and was prepared to wait until she was ready to marry him.

'So,' he finished off with a loving look at Amy. 'I figure I have to start my whole life from scratch. I've got to find a job and a place to live. I guess that has to be my first priority.'

Jed was incredulous. 'You've given up a fantastic job, your whole way of life, even your family, not to mention your former fiancée — all for our Amy?'

'And I don't regret any of it,' Mike said softly, squeezing Amy's hand and gazing into her eyes. 'So long as Amy's with me, I'm happy.'

'But are you quite sure your father wants nothing to do with you?' Jed went on. If the boot were on the other foot, he couldn't imagine ever being so cruel as to cut off any of his children, no matter how much he disapproved of what they were doing.

'I'm pretty certain he doesn't want to know me right now.' Mike lowered his eyes, unable to hide the fact that he was hurt by his father's bitter reaction. 'Dad's a proud man and Kari's family are proud, too. And pride can some-times be pretty destructive. Besides, they've been friendly for so long. I can't see Dad backing down, not yet anyway.'

'What about your mother, Mike?' Sheila asked.

'Oh, Mom will stick by Dad, no matter what.'

There was an awkward silence. The Palmers felt really sorry for Mike, but Amy was still their main concern.

'I guess I'll just have to prove to my father that I can stand on my own two feet.' Mike grinned. 'And I'm sure that once he gets to know Amy, he'll love her as much as I do.'

'So what are you going to do for the moment, lad?' Jed asked. 'What can you do? I know you're some kind of business executive, but can you get that kind of work in this country? Won't it all be different over here?'

'Oh, it's not so different.' Mike smiled. 'But I'm not interested in going back to that kind of work right now. I reckon I need a change from all that high-powered stuff. I figure if I can get back to nature for a while, take stock and all that, maybe I'll find out where I'm headed. Maybe it's not such a big deal for me to be making lots of money all the time.' His eyes clouded. 'The point is, I've got to get by somehow. I'll miss the security, of course I will, but I'm prepared to have a go at anything. Besides, even though it gives me a buzz, I don't want to have to go to a city to work. I want to stay right here, so I can be near Amy.'

Amy blushed. 'Mike, you're embarrassing me.'

'Sorry.' Mike grinned. 'I guess I just can't help the way I feel about you.' Then, solemnly, he turned to address Jed. 'I'd appreciate any work you can give me, sir. I guess I'll have to see about applying for a permit to stay in this country.'

'Well, I won't deny I could do with some extra help.' Jed shrugged his shoulders. 'Especially with me being laid up. I can't pay you much, mind. But you'll get your keep and food and a bit over besides. Can't promise you more than that.'

'That'll suit me, Mr Palmer. So is it a deal?'

Jed grinned and shook Mike firmly by the hand. 'It's a deal. We'll give it a try. Now we've sorted out how you're going to earn your living, as a stop-gap at least, we'll have to give some thought to where you're going to stay. We can't expect you to go on sleeping in a tent.'

'That's not a problem, Ted,' Sheila put in. 'There's always the spare room. I'll get it ready.'

'Thanks, Mrs Palmer,' Mike interrupted, 'but I'd rather not, so long as you won't be offended. You've already been more generous than I deserve. Besides, the novelty of having a house guest might just wear off quicker than you think. But if you don't mind my butting in, I've been giving the problem some thought.' He smiled disarmingly. 'If you're agreeable, I wondered if I could move into that old cottage in the trees behind the meadow. I've had a look at it and I know it's run-down, but I'd genuinely love to live there.'

'But it's derelict, Mike,' Sheila said. 'No one's lived there for donkey's years. I'm not even sure it's safe.'

'The building's sound enough, I suppose,' Jed wavered.

'It's in a great spot,' Mike enthused, 'and I'm pretty good with my hands. I'd like the chance to carry out the repairs that it needs.'

'Fair enough. You've just found yourself a cottage to live in.' Jed laughed. 'You should be able to find most of the materials you need for repairs around the farm. And I've just remembered something else. Old Fred Barstow from Stoneybrook Farm was asking the other day if I could spare one of my lads to do some casual work for him. You could give him a hand, too.'

'Well, that's that settled,' Sheila said, standing up. 'Shall we have a drink to celebrate?'

'No time, Mum.' Amy jumped up, giving Mike a peck on the cheek. 'I'm late for work already.'

'We could stroll down to look at the cottage, Mike,' Jed suggested. 'I haven't had a proper look at it for a long time.'

'Jed . . . '

'It's all right, Mrs Palmer.' Mike grinned. 'I'll take care of him.'

Amy grabbed her bag and rushed to the door. 'See you later,' she called cheerfully.

★ ★ ★

'You should have seen him!' Sam Threadwell chortled. 'I can't get over it. Soaked to the skin he was, and chasing his tent all around the field.'

'Don't be rotten, Sam,' Amy chuckled. 'Poor Mike! It must have been an awful experience for him.'

They were still laughing when Phil Scott came in. He was a tall, dark-haired man in his early 30s. Despite the fact that he'd lived locally for several years, he was still considered by some to be an outsider. Sam waved him over. 'Come and have a pint with us, Phil,' he called. 'A drop of the good stuff.'

Phil laughed. 'Oh no you don't. I've lived here too long to fall for that one.'

'Suit yourself,' Sam said innocently. 'Shan't twist your arm.'

Some of the locals had resented Phil

Scott at first when he'd bought the big manor house and turned it into a holiday complex and leisure centre. But fortunately, he'd soon settled in and become accepted by most. 'So, how's my favourite barmaid?' He grinned at Amy. 'I must say, you're looking particularly pretty tonight. Wouldn't you say, Sam?'

'Certainly would. Prettiest lass in the whole northwest, I'd say.'

Amy coloured and laughingly shrugged off the compliment. She was in her element — serving, chatting and joking with her regulars — when Kari Reynolds suddenly walked into the bar.

Silence fell briefly as everyone turned to look at the beautiful stranger. She looked absolutely stunning in a short, fitted, backless black dress. Amy's heart seemed to drop to the pit of her stomach. How could Mike prefer a simple country girl like her, to this gorgeous, sophisticated woman?

Kari seemed totally unperturbed by all the attention and it dawned on Amy that she must be used to it. She fixed her eyes on Amy and walked slowly towards the bar. People moved aside to let her through until, at last, she was standing face-to-face with Amy across the bar.

'Hi,' she said, her tone disarmingly friendly. 'So this is where you work. What a coincidence, bumping into you like this. I was so parched, I had to call in for a drink. Something refreshing.'

Amy felt as if she could hardly breathe, her heart hammering behind her ribs. Kari was even more beautiful close up than she'd first thought. 'What can I get you?' she said at last, her voice no more than a whisper.

Kari's smile widened and, for a moment, Amy was lulled into a false sense of well-being; but when Kari told her what she wanted, her face fell.

'I'd like a cocktail. Make it a Presidente, thank you.'

'I . . . I'm sorry, I've never heard of that,' Amy was forced to admit. 'We don't go in for a wide range of cocktails. There's not much demand for that sort of drink round here.'

Kari's smile was long-suffering and she made sure everyone saw it. She turned back to Amy. 'It's really quite simple.' Her voice was undeniably patronising. 'You shouldn't have too much trouble mixing it.' Her laugh was mocking, no doubt about it.

'Perhaps you'd like to tell me what's in it,' Amy said politely. 'I'm willing to have a go.'

'Sure.' Kari spoke slowly, as if Amy might have difficulty understanding. 'Dry Vermouth and white rum in equal measures.' She turned to the regulars. 'Plus a dash of grenadine and curacao. It really couldn't be simpler. Then all you do is shake it and stir in plenty of crushed ice.'

Hands trembling, Amy mixed the drink, certain that it wouldn't measure up to Kari's standards.

'That looks just fine,' Kari said. 'Thank you so much.' Her tone was condescending.

She paid for her drink and carried it away from the crowded bar to an empty table, perfectly aware that all eyes were on her. Then gradually, to Amy's astonishment, one by one, the men at the bar drifted over to Kari's table like moths around a candle.

'I wish I'd received such a warm welcome when I was new in town,' Phil remarked drily.

'Perhaps you don't have such nice legs,' Amy laughed.

Phil grinned ruefully and, picking up his drink, he excused himself and joined the others at Kari's table.

★   ★   ★

Kari had already singled him out as different from the rest, although they were all nice and friendly. Some of them, like the man called Sam, were openly curious about her. Phil Scott, on the other hand, was cool and poised. Although he said little, Kari was well aware that she intrigued him. He

116

watched her every move with his granite eyes; and the attention of this handsome man, more than anyone else's, gave a much-needed boost to her self-esteem.

Outwardly, Kari was very confident, but inside she was lost and alone. Her laughter, she was sure, had a false ring. Once or twice, she looked towards the bar and saw Amy standing alone and watching thoughtfully.

'Cheer up, lass,' Sam remarked when he went to the bar to order more drinks. 'You look as though you've lost a pound and found a penny.'

Amy mustered a smile. 'Won't Kate be expecting you home?' she said.

'Probably.' He grinned wickedly.

'I don't know how she puts up with you.' Amy shook her head.

'Oh, she'll understand.' He shrugged. 'Wait until I tell her about that American girl. Do you know her? She seemed to know you.'

'She's very beautiful.' Amy clenched her teeth.

'I wonder what she's doing here. Something to do with Mike, do you think?'

'I wouldn't know, Sam,' Amy said briefly. 'Is that all?'

Gales of laughter came from the corner, where Kari was almost obscured by her crowd of admirers. What was she up to? Amy was sure that more than thirst had brought Kari into the Ram's Head. It wouldn't have required a great deal of detective work to find out that she worked here.

Her unease grew as the evening wore on. Just when she thought everything was starting to make sense, this had to happen.

The only thing she could be sure of was that Kari was up to something.

Towards the end of the evening, Amy took a tray round, collecting empty glasses. She knew she'd eventually have to face Kari's table. She'd allowed the glasses to pile up enough already. Finally, gathering up all her courage, she went over to the table, determined not to allow Kari to upset her. There was only one way she knew of doing that, and that was to say something first, before Kari could make any kind of barbed comment.

With a fixed smile on her face, Amy said, 'Well, it certainly hasn't taken you any time at all to get to know people.'

Kari nodded, and her voice was soft and steady as she looked Amy straight in the eye. 'Maybe not. But, frankly, I'm not very interested in them.' Her smile was mocking. 'You know as well as I do that there's only one man I'm interested in. And I always get what I want, Amy. You can be sure of that.'

# 5

The smooth white walls of the large, sprawling mansion were bathed in the warm amber glow of the morning sun. Inside, Barbara Carter was distractedly putting down the telephone. In all the years she had lived in Virginia as Michael Carter's wife, she'd never felt so downhearted and defeated.

Until recently, her life had seemed to be almost charmed, blessed with happiness and good fortune. But now, it all seemed to be falling apart. Her eyes, brimming with tears, reflected her sadness, but she was quick to blink them away and regain her composure as she heard her husband's approach. Her hand, however, still rested on the telephone receiver as Michael Carter Senior breezed into the room.

'Hi, honey. Was that the phone?' He kissed her cheek. 'I'm expecting a call from Jack.' He headed straight for the bar in the corner and tossed ice into a glass. 'Can I fix you one?'

'No, thank you, dear.' Barbara watched him pour bourbon over the ice, and it was a moment or two before he became aware of her reflective scrutiny.

'What's up?' he said, shrugging. 'Did I say something? Did I forget something?'

'Oh, Michael.' Barbara sighed deeply before she spoke. 'That was Mike on the phone. You remember Mike, don't you? He's your son.'

As had become the norm lately, at the mention of his son's name Michael Carter switched off, but Barbara strode over to him and gripped his arm, forcing him to look at her.

'Hear me out, Michael,' she pleaded. 'Do you realise how much all this is hurting him, too? Can't we at least lift these silly restrictions on his money?'

'He's called you? To ask for money?' His voice was incredulous.

'No, of course not!' Barbara said crossly. 'He called to find out if we were all right. He's worried about us, Michael. We're his parents. He cares about us — even if you don't care about him.'

Michael Carter put his drink down and covered Barbara's hand with his. For a moment she thought he was going to relent.

'Honey, I understand how you feel,' he said quietly. 'And I would do anything for that boy, anything at all, but the fact is he's let us down badly. And most of all he's let Kari down. What that poor girl has gone through — is going through — is anybody's guess. No, he's on his own. He chose to put himself in this position, Barbara; we didn't. I know it's hard for you to take, honey, and for him. And it is without doubt the hardest thing I've ever had to do. But I don't think we should intervene, except in a real emergency.'

Barbara knew it was pointless to argue. Besides, she'd always stood by her husband, fallen into line and trusted him to make the right decisions.

'I do know how you feel,' he said softly, and she could see heartfelt understanding and sympathy in his eyes. 'But it may not be a bad thing for Mike to stand on his own two feet for once, just like I had to do. It'll be the making of him if he can start from scratch. I've got every faith in him.'

'And if he doesn't make it?'

'He'll come to his senses sooner or later,' Michael said confidently. 'Trust me, honey. Mike will come around, just as soon as he sees how foolish he's being.'

★　★　★

A bird fluttered out through a hole in the roof, startling Mike so that he had to scrabble to regain his balance. He'd been working on the repairs to the roof all afternoon and he was almost there. While he caught his breath, he looked around in amazement. He hadn't realised the view was so spectacular from the top of his ladder. The distant Cumbrian mountains formed a blue-grey backdrop to the lush green of nearer hills, the colours darkening and intensifying as black storm clouds gathered in the distance. As he drank in the dramatic scene, he had the strangest feeling that there was something very special about this place. Although he was an American from the other side of the world, for some unaccountable reason he had this intense feeling of belonging.

A spot of rain hitting him in the face brought him back to the present with a jolt. Those black clouds were overhead now, casting shadows over the entire landscape, turning the water of the lake to liquid silver. Right now, the most important thing in his life was getting the roof repairs completed before the deluge started.

'No wonder Mom sounded worried and upset,' he muttered to himself. This time last month, he'd been at ease handling millions of dollars of clients' money. Now he wielded a hammer and a handful of nails, and didn't feel half as confident.

Suddenly, the sky all about him flashed with streaks of lightning, followed moments later by the low rumble of thunder beyond the mountains. Time to call it a day, he decided. At least the rain wouldn't get in through the slates now. The rest of the outside work could wait until another fine day.

As he started to descend the ladder, a car drew up. Turning, he saw it was Jed Palmer's Land Rover. Sheila was driving, Jed was sitting beside her and Amy was in the back. They all waved and piled out, heedless of the rain. Mike was touched with warmth for these caring, friendly people.

It was going to be well worth it, this dramatic change of lifestyle. Even major setbacks were a small price to pay for loving Amy.

'Hello there, Mike! How's it going?' Jed called.

'Leave that, Jed!' Sheila barked at her husband as he began to wrestle with a box in the car. 'We'll manage it. You just get Mike to open the door for us.'

'What's all this?' Mike asked, helping to carry boxes into the cottage.

'Oh, Mum found a few things up at the house she thought you may find useful,' Amy told him. She opened up one of the boxes. 'Look, we've got some pretty curtains and a nice rug and some cups and plates. Oh, and a vase for flowers. You know, just a few things to make the place a little more homely.'

Mike burst out laughing and Amy looked puzzled. 'Back home,' he explained, 'if you say something's homely, you mean it's unattractive. Crazy language, English.'

Amy chuckled in agreement.

'And here are some groceries for you,' Sheila put in. 'Just to tide you over. Are you sure you're all right here, Mike?' she added, looking round. 'I mean, this place hasn't been lived in for donkey's years. It's probably damp and draughty.' She sounded concerned. 'I know you've got running water, but everything else is pretty basic and there's no heating. It'll get really cold in the winter. You'll be chipping ice off the inside of the windows just to see out.' She stopped unpacking the box and looked around, frowning. 'The thing is, you know you can come back home with us any time. We've got the spare room.'

'You've been more than generous to me already, both of you,' he said, looking gratefully at Jed and Sheila. He smiled his wide, open smile. 'Now what do I owe you out of my first pay packet?'

'Don't be daft, lad.' Sheila brushed his question aside.

Jed, who had been watching and listening and saying very little, put his hand on Sheila's shoulder. 'Look, love, I can see what Mike's driving at,' he said gently. 'He wants to stand on his own two feet. I can understand that, can't you? You have to admire him for it. Fair enough, Mike. If that's how you want it, you can pay for the groceries.'

'All right.' Sheila's eyes were bright, her cheeks flushed. She was finding all this rather exciting, and it was good to see the old cottage being put to good use. 'You can make us a cup of tea and then we'll leave you to sort out where you want to put everything. Right, Jed?' She nudged him in the ribs. 'I was saying we'll get off home in a minute and leave the young people on their own for a while.'

'I can't stay,' Amy put in, looking uncomfortably at Mike and catching the disappointment in his eyes. 'I have to work at the pub tonight,' she said ruefully.

'Well, we'll just get these curtains up,' Sheila said briskly, draining her cup. 'Men are hopeless at that sort of thing. Then we'll be off.'

By the time they left, there was a pretty cloth on the circular table and some pink dog roses in the vase in the centre. With curtains at the window and the rug in front of the fireplace, at least the place seemed warmer and more welcoming and definitely more homely.

'I don't think this rain will last long,' Sheila remarked, hitching her coat up over her head. 'I can see a patch of blue sky.'

'Bye, Mike.' Amy reached up and kissed him softly on the cheek. 'You'll manage to unpack yourself, won't you?' she asked impishly. Then she was gone, running and splashing through the puddles to the car.

Dejectedly, Mike stood at the door, watching as the Land Rover drove off through the rain. It was coming down in sheets now, blotting out the land-scape. After his hard day fixing the roof, he'd hoped Amy would be able to stay and spend some time with him.

Back inside the cottage, he busied himself unpacking the boxes of provi-sions. At least he knew he wouldn't go hungry. By the time he'd finished, the rain had stopped. He looked out and saw a vehicle flashing through the trees, coming towards the cottage.

A small shiver of anticipation shot through him. Who could it be? Surely Kari hadn't found out about this place?

He opened up the front door and felt relieved to see the Land Rover, relief turning to joy when he saw Amy was at the wheel, and alone. Excitedly, he opened the door. She waved, jumped out, then carefully picked up a box.

'More stuff?' Mike said, astonished.

'Yes! All for you. There's another load in the boot. Could you bring it in?'

He fetched it from the car and followed her back into the cottage. 'I thought you had to work,' he said.

'Disappointed?' she asked.

He grinned. 'Not on your life.'

A huge smile lit up her face. 'This is a special present from me.' She opened her box and carefully lifted out a velvety black puppy. 'And from Bracken — to you.' She presented Mike with the puppy, who immediately began to lick and nibble at Mike's fingers. His little tail quivered in delirious joy.

'Want to have a look round, fella?'

Mike said, gently placing the pup on the floor. He snuffled around fearlessly, sniffing new smells, exploring his new surroundings, not seeming to be missing his mother or his brothers and sisters at all.

Amy sat down on the old rug and Mike settled down beside her. For a while they watched the puppy's progress as he stopped to play chase with a piece of cardboard box.

'Amy, he's gorgeous,' Mike whispered. 'I'll take good care of him, I promise.'

'You'd better,' Amy laughed. 'You'll never be lonely now, but he's your responsibility, don't forget. You'll have to make sure he gets all his inoculations and take him for walks, rain or shine. And when you're working, he can come up to the farm house so he won't get lonely.'

Mike grinned. 'I'll do right by him, don't worry. What'll we call him?'

She laughed. 'Oh, you'll think of something.'

'Amy.' Mike was waiting as she straightened up. He looked down lovingly at her, letting his fingers trail lingeringly down the length of her bare arm. 'I want to thank you for all you and your family have done for me,' he whispered. 'I mean it. I don't know what I'd have done without you.' He put his arm around her shoulders and led her to the old, shabby, comfortable sofa which sagged beneath them as they sat down. She leaned blissfully against him, feeling safe and warm and protected in his arms.

'How long have you been here, Mike?'

'I don't know.' He shrugged. 'Three weeks, more? I've lost all track of time since I came over here. All I know is that it's been the best time of my life.'

'It seems longer,' Amy murmured. 'So much has happened. Dad's heart attack. It hardly seems possible to see him looking so well again so quickly. When I think what he looked like when I first saw him in hospital . . . ' She shuddered. 'Apart from that, I feel that I've known you longer, Mike. I just can't imagine not knowing you.'

'If I have my way,' Mike tilted her chin so that he could gaze into her eyes, 'you'll have the rest of your life to get to know me.'

*This is real*, Amy thought suddenly. *He's serious. It's not just romantic small talk.* Her mind was in a whirl. She no longer felt frightened and anxious, but pleased and excited. Misty-eyed, she returned his tender, lingering kiss.

'It's getting late, Mike,' she murmured softly. 'Time for bed.'

Mike looked at her cheekily and grinned. 'Why, Amy, I thought you'd never ask.'

Amy laughed, blushing prettily as she pushed him playfully away. 'You're going to need all your strength for getting up at four o'clock tomorrow morning. It's your turn on the milking. Besides, I'll have to get going.'

Mike groaned in mock agony and fell back against the sofa, as Amy's laughter rang around the room.

★　★　★

Kari pulled on her smooth cream leather driving gloves and slipped behind the wheel of her hired car. She just couldn't sit around in that hotel room doing nothing any longer.

For a moment she sat in the hotel car park, drumming her fingers impatiently against the wheel, trying to make up her mind what to do. She knew what she wanted to do. She wanted to drive right on up to that farm where Mike was supposedly working for the Palmer girl's father and talk to him. Yet she was seized by an uncharacteristic lack of confidence, which she wanted to get under control before there was any kind of confrontation.

The hotel was halfway up a hill, positioned so that it faced both the lake and the village. Kari looked down the twisting, narrow road to those tiny, rose-clad cottages which lined cobbled streets, and knew in her heart that the Mike she knew so well could never fit in here.

He was a city boy born and bred, and

he belonged in the world of business, living on a razor's edge, relying on his skill and wit. OK, so he was into the great outdoors in a big way and was a keen sportsman, but tramping muddy fields with a bucket of cattle fodder in his hand was hardly his scene.

Her lip curved into a smile of genuine amusement as this comical picture flashed into her mind. As her thoughts boosted her confidence, she felt ready now to meet Mike.

The road up to the farm was full of tricky twists and turns and dangerous corners, making Kari wish for the long, wide, fast highways back home. She was driving so quickly that she almost missed the sign for the farm and her brakes screeched as she took the turning too fast, startling chickens, ducks and geese and sending them scurrying noisily in all directions.

She drew up outside the farmhouse and stepped out of the car, turning up her nose at the pungent farmyard smells.

Sheila Palmer banged the oven door shut and wiped her arm across her forehead. She had the farm all to herself for a while with Jed and her sons off at auction. Amy was helping at the Ram's Head and Mike was working over at Fred Barstow's place, Stoneybrook, and so Sheila had taken the chance to catch up on her batch-baking. If she were honest, she'd done it with Mike in mind, too. She'd tell him that the freezer was full and that he'd be doing her a favour taking it off her bands, if he tried to protest.

Movement outside in the yard caught her eye. Curious, she turned down the radio and went to the window. The young woman wandering uncertainly around the yard was a stranger to Sheila. The first thing that Sheila noticed was that she was very elegant and very beautiful. Sheila gasped in astonishment as it dawned on her who it was. Amy had described Kari Reynolds to her and this lovely girl fitted the bill to a T.

Quickly, she removed her apron, patted her hair into place and rinsed her hands. If only she'd had some warning about this. Heart fluttering, she stepped out into the yard.

'Hello there.' She smiled. 'Can I help you?'

'Hi.' Kari turned and strolled over to her and Sheila was struck by the girl's poise and style. She had no doubt in her mind that this was Kari.

'My name's Kari Reynolds. I'm Mike Carter's fiancée. You must be Amy's mother. I'd like a few words with Mike, if you could just tell him I'm here.'

Sheila was struck speechless for a moment. It was bad enough hearing this girl describing herself as Mike's fiancée, without being spoken to in such a superior way. She decided that the girl was probably coming over in this high-handed way because she'd been hurt.

She mustered her most pleasant smile. 'I'm sorry, Miss Reynolds, but Mike's not here. He's helping out on one of our neighbour's farms. In fact, I'm the only one here, I'm afraid.'

For a fleeting moment, Sheila glimpsed something in the disappointed expression that flitted across Kari's face which reminded her in some ridiculous way of her own daughter. It was a daft thought, of course. Amy was completely different from Kari. And yet, something in that surprised, vulnerable look reminded Sheila that Kari was just a young girl too — not perhaps as assured as she'd like others to believe — and alone, too, in a strange country.

Looking again at this cool confident girl, perhaps her sympathy was misplaced, but she just couldn't find it within herself to turn her away out of hand.

'Look, if you have time, come in for a cup of tea and a chat. I've just made some fresh scones, too.' She gave Kari a friendly smile. 'How about it?'

Kari looked taken aback, but nodded and allowed Sheila to lead her into the big, warm farmhouse kitchen.

'It smells heavenly,' Kari remarked, and her eyes widened at the sight of the cooling racks piled high with scones, bread and golden-crust pies.

'Have a seat, dear.' Kari found Sheila Palmer surprisingly easy to talk to. The woman was warm and friendly and seemed genuinely anxious to put the stranger at her ease.

Kari hadn't come here intending to cause trouble, but when Sheila Palmer presented her with such an opportunity, she couldn't resist stirring things up.

'Look, lass . . . ' Sheila began. 'I know it can't be easy to see the lad you love fall for someone else.'

Kari looked at her, wide-eyed and innocent, nervously twisting the sparkling ring on her engagement finger. 'Oh, Mrs Palmer, don't worry on that score.' Kari's tone was surprisingly nonchalant and Sheila was momentarily confused. 'There's no way I'm bitter about what's happened, and I can assure you I bear no malice towards your daughter. The thing is, Mike's a charmer, a romantic dreamer, and well . . . ' She sighed and gave Sheila a long-suffering conspiratorial look. 'I have to tell you this isn't the first time he's done this.'

'What? What do you mean?' Sheila breathed, hardly believing what she was hearing. Could she really have read everything so terribly wrong?

'I guess Mike's always had a . . . a weakness for a pretty girl,' Kari continued softly. 'But once the initial thrill of the chase wears off, he comes back to me. He always does,' she ended resignedly.

Sheila Palmer was silent now. The colour had drained from her face.

Kari continued to speak, and although her voice was calm and steady, her heart was thundering. 'Please don't get me wrong. Mike doesn't set out to hurt anyone. He's like an overgrown kid at times.' She sighed wearily. 'You must have noticed how immature he is.'

Sheila Palmer stared at the American girl, suddenly seeing past her sophisticated beauty and her expensive clothes.

She should have realised. Kari and Mike were from a different world. How could he possibly be happy with his current situation — no money and a run-down old cottage — when he had always had the very best money could buy?

They'd been living in a dream world, all of them.

Fear gripped her — fear for her daughter. She'd had her heart broken not all that long ago. She didn't deserve all that hurt again when Mike tired of her. 'Why exactly are you here, Miss Reynolds?' she asked icily. 'What do you want from us?'

Kari stood up. Her smile was cool. 'It's quite simple. I want him back. And I'll get him, don't you worry on that score. Thanks for the tea, Mrs Palmer,' she said softly. 'And the sympathy. But you should save it for your daughter. She's the one who's going to need it.'

Outside, she quickly crossed the yard to her car and got inside. She couldn't believe how well things had gone just now. Her heart was hammering in her

chest and her stomach was full of
butterflies, but she felt good and at the
same time bad that she'd told such
awful lies about Mike. He had never
been the cheating kind, which was why
this had come as such an awful shock.

But she'd given Amy Palmer's mother
something to think about. A black
Labrador bitch came out of the barn
and barked twice — low, deep barks
— but her tail was wagging. She
padded over to the car and Kari
reached out to stroke her soft head.

'I bet Mike's really taken with you.'
She smiled and briefly she could understand how this place had distracted him.
But it was only temporary. He'd soon
tire of this sleepy backwater.

★ ★ ★

Phil Scott sat alone at the hotel bar.
He'd spent the morning sailing his boat
on the lake and had come ashore raven-
ously hungry and incredibly thirsty.
The linen jeans and white shirt he wore

emphasised the depth of his tan and the tawny colour of his hair, but when Kari Reynolds walked through the bar she didn't even give him a sideways glance.

He watched her walk by, thinking she looked even lovelier than she had the other night in the Ram's Head. Her grey-green eyes were ablaze, her dark hair glinted as she walked, and today there was something so vital about her. She reminded him of a big cat — sleek, slinky and incredibly beautiful — but dangerous, too.

'Your table's ready, Mr Scott.'

'Uh?' Phil Scott turned reluctantly. 'Oh, thanks.' He glanced back in time to see the lift doors swishing shut behind Kari Reynolds. Thoughtfully, he finished his drink before making his way unhurriedly towards the restaurant.

That was one young lady he decided he'd very much like to get to know better.

★　★　★

'You know,' Jed stated that evening at the dinner table, 'I bet there's nothing that young man wouldn't tackle if he put his mind to it. Mike's obviously right at home here,' he enthused. 'I think he's going to fit in just fine.'

'Maybe.' Sheila sniffed. 'It's early days yet to be making remarks like that. Time will tell.'

Amy was oblivious to her mother's sudden doubts where Mike was concerned. All she heard was her father's praise for Mike, and it pleased her more than she would ever have thought possible.

Although no-one seemed to notice, Sheila hardly ate at all and was quiet throughout the meal. The more she thought of her encounter with Kari Reynolds, the more she realised Amy and Mike were worlds apart.

After the meal, Jed went off with his evening paper, blissfully unaware of his wife's dilemma.

'I think I'll just pop over to the cottage and say goodnight to Mike,' Amy remarked later as she helped her mother with the dishes. 'I'd like to see the pup, too.' Her eyes shone. 'I wonder if Mike's got a name for him yet.'

Sheila turned her troubled eyes away from her daughter. Seeing Amy's obvious happiness increased her anxiety. She couldn't tell Amy what Kari had said about Mike. It would devastate her, but she had to warn her.

'Amy, love,' she said softly, placing her hand firmly on her daughter's arm. 'Promise me you won't rush into anything too serious with Mike. I . . . I know he's attractive and charming and he seems to be madly in love with you, but . . . well, just remember you haven't known him long. What I mean is . . . just be careful, won't you?'

'Oh, Mum, you are in a funny mood tonight.' Amy hugged her tight, loving her for her concern. 'You don't have to worry about me. I'm a big girl now. I can take care of myself.'

Sheila watched her eldest daughter go and, with a worried sigh, whispered to herself, 'Can you? I'm not so sure, love.'

★ ★ ★

The door to the cottage was unlocked and Amy let herself in carefully, in case the pup heard her and got out. She needn't have worried. The puppy was curled up beside Mike on the old, sagging sofa. Both were sound asleep.

She reached out to touch Mike in a rush of love for him. He looked so young, so good-looking, so . . . everything. Looking at him, so relaxed and at peace with the world, she knew she loved him, really truly loved him. His eyes opened suddenly, and seeing the love in them thrilled her.

'Amy!' His look was so tender that her heart quickened. He looked exhausted, but he reached out for her hand and pulled her to him. 'Amy, will you marry me — please?'

She knew she wanted to say yes, yes she would marry him now, tomorrow, next week . . .

She opened her mouth to reply, but

suddenly she remembered her mother's words of concern. *Promise me you won't rush into anything.*

'I'll think about it,' she said teasingly.

# 6

Amy watched her mother going about her morning chores in the kitchen. There was a briskness about her manner, as if something was bothering her.

'Mum?' Sheila looked up and Amy thought that her smile was a little too quick, forced even.

'Yes, love?'

'The other night when you told me not to rush into anything with Mike. What brought that on? I thought you really liked Mike.'

Sheila hadn't mentioned Kari Reynolds' visit to anyone and had no intention of upsetting Amy by telling her about it now. She turned her back for a moment to put a pan on the cooker.

'Mum?'

'Oh.' Sheila turned back, a concerned smile on her face. 'I do like Mike. I just meant that, well, I wouldn't want to see you go through all that heartbreak again. You know, after Alan . . . '

'Oh, come on, Mum, this is different. Mike's nothing like Alan. You know that. Mike's serious about our relationship, and you've always told me to go with my feelings and listen to my heart. Like you and Dad, remember?' Amy felt good being able to talk about Alan without it hurting. If Mike had done that for her already in the short time she'd known him, it was more than a step forward; it was a giant leap.

'I know, love. But you must be sure of your feelings before you allow yourself to trust them. Mike's asked you to marry him, hasn't he?' She fought to keep the anxiety out of her voice.

'Yes, but I haven't given him my answer yet. I do love him, Mum, but I told him I need a little more time, because it's all happened so fast.'

'It's not that.' Sheila sniffed and

ruffled Amy's hair affectionately. 'Sorry, love, I'm being a killjoy. All I want is for you to be happy like your dad and I have been.'

* ★ ★

'Fool!' Kari growled to herself as she struggled against the breeze to open a road map on the bonnet of her hire car. She couldn't believe she'd managed to get herself lost or that her hire car hadn't got a satellite navigation system. The map hardly made any sense to her at all and, in the end, in a fit of frustration, she scrunched it up and threw it into the back seat of the car. All she'd wanted to do was escape the tourist traps. She'd done that all right. Now here she was, in the middle of nowhere and with no idea which way to go.

She stood, hands on hips, surveying her surroundings. She was still close to the lake — she could see the shimmering water through the trees — but she had completely lost her bearings.

She was dressed casually in white leggings and a figure-hugging T-shirt. Then, pushing her sunglasses on top of her head, she turned around and noticed a sign for a holiday and leisure complex offering a wide range of sports facilities.

Moments later, her curiosity roused, Kari was back in the car. As she drove in through the entrance gates, and up the tree-lined drive, she could hardly believe her eyes. 'Now this is more like it!' She smiled to herself.

Attractive chalets nestled discreetly among the trees. No wonder she had driven past without noticing it. The main building was a former stately home, its grey stone walls covered in rich ruby Virginia creeper. Huge towers rose skywards and the sun glinted on the mullioned windows. 'Wow!' she breathed in delight.

Steps led up to a magnificent pillared entrance, where tubs and hanging baskets spilled a glorious display of red and gold summer flowers. She paused before going inside. From here it was impossible to see any of the cabins, but there was a wonderful view of the lake and the distant mist-shrouded mountains.

She stepped into a cool hallway. Inside, the house retained its wonderful character, from the polished parquet floor to the magnificent curving oak staircase with its ornate balustrade.

'May I help you?' Kari spun round and noticed the young woman sitting behind a reception desk. 'Good morning,' she said with a welcoming smile as Kari walked towards her. 'How can I help?'

'Hi.' Kari smiled. 'This place — ' she spread her hands. ' — it's wonderful. I'd no idea it existed. In fact, I came upon it quite by accident. Actually, it's the sporting facilities I'm interested in. I'm staying nearby in a hotel. Do you have to be a resident here to enjoy the facilities?'

'Not at all.' The girl smiled. 'We can

offer you temporary membership, which will entitle you to full use of everything.' She stood up and walked to a notice board, where a number of leaflets were displayed. 'Is there anything you're particularly interested in, Miss er . . . ?'

'Reynolds, Kari Reynolds.' Kari smiled. 'Can you tell me what's on offer?'

'I can indeed, and I'm Carol Taylor,' the girl returned. She smiled pleasantly. 'The owner of the centre is very keen on conserving nature,' she told Kari as she selected various leaflets from the pigeonholes beneath the board. 'And he's very proud of the fact that not one single tree had to be chopped down in the development of this place.'

'Well, that's an admirable achievement these days when so many people are out to make a fast buck.' Kari nodded her approval enthusiastically.

'Here. You'll find something in this to interest you, I'm sure.' Carol Taylor handed over the leaflets.

'Hello there!' A voice from behind startled Kari. She spun round, sure she recognised this man, but unable in that instant to place him.

'Phil Scott.' He grinned, holding out his hand and grasping hers in a firm, business-like shake. 'We've already met, last night in the pub. Remember?'

'Oh, yes! Forgive me.' She smiled. 'I've met so many new people over these past few days.' Although she wondered now, as she looked at this very attractive man, how she could have forgotten him.

'I was just giving Miss Reynolds a few leaflets,' the receptionist said. Then, turning to address Kari, she added, 'Mr Scott is the owner of this complex. It's his baby.'

'Really? How interesting.' Kari turned to Phil. 'Actually, I tumbled across this place by sheer accident. I've been doing a little exploring round and . . . well, to be honest, I was trying to get away from the tourists and ended up getting myself lost.'

'Well, if it's peace and quiet you're after, you've come to the right place. Why don't you allow me to show you

154

around?' he suggested smoothly. 'There's a lot to see.'

It wasn't in Kari's nature to demur. Besides, she was getting tired of her own company. 'I'd love that.' She smiled.

'If you're stuck for things to do in the evenings,' Carol Taylor put in, 'the night life around here's not too bad either. The pubs are quite lively and friendly and, in fact, there's a dance on tonight. It's an annual do and absolutely everyone goes to it. It's always great fun. I'm sure you'd love it.'

'Well,' Kari said, 'it would certainly make a change from room service at my hotel.'

'Actually,' Carol said thoughtfully, 'when I think about it, I'll bet that nice young American guy will be there. He's a friend of Amy Palmer — she's a local lass — so at least you'd have someone else from the States to chat to. And he's a bit of a hunk too.'

Kari's heart sank, knowing Carol must mean Mike, especially when spoken in the same breath as Amy Palmer's name.

So they'd be there, too, would they? Her eyes narrowed. Perhaps she should go along, not just to get out of the hotel, as she'd implied, but to make things as uncomfortable as possible for Amy and Mike.

'Sure, I'd love to go to the dance,' she said brightly.

'Why don't you come along with me, Kari,' Phil suggested. 'I'd be honoured.'

Kari's delighted smile thrilled him. 'Why, thank you!' she said. 'I'd love to come with you, Phil.'

Phil Scott could hardly believe his luck. A date with the beautiful, intriguing Kari Reynolds. He found her really fascinating and exciting, and he was looking forward to getting to know her better.

* * *

Mike strolled along the edge of the field, his senses filled with the sweet scents and sounds of his surroundings. He looked fit and tanned. His shirt sleeves were rolled up, his jacket was slung over his shoulder and he was charged with a powerful sense of well-being. Tired after a long day working in the fields, but content with the knowledge of a job well done, he whistled softly as he walked and didn't notice Jed Palmer standing at the end of the field, watching him, until he'd drawn level.

'How's it going, lad?' he enquired.

'Hi! Oh, fine, Jed. I've never been so physically exhausted in my life, but I feel good, real good.'

'Well, you're looking great on it.' Jed grinned. 'I can't wait to get back to work myself. All this taking it easy lark is driving me mad. By the way, how's the work on the cottage coming along?'

'It's slow, but I'm getting there. I'm really pleased with what I've done so far. Why don't you come along and take a look? You got time?'

'Why not? Sheila won't be expecting me home just yet.'

Together, they took a leisurely stroll to the cottage in the late afternoon sunshine.

157

Mike was eager to show off his handiwork and pleased at Jed's reaction.

'I'd never have thought it possible.' Jed smiled his craggy smile and cast his expert eye over Mike's handiwork. 'And you, a city boy! I like the way you've replaced those old rotting window frames. And you've done a grand job on the roof.'

Mike's Labrador pup pranced up to greet Jed. 'I swear he's grown since he came to live with you.' Jed laughed. 'What are you feeding him on? Best steak? Amy says you'll be bringing him up to the house tonight while you and she go to the dance,' Jed went on. 'So Bracken will be pup-sitting for you.'

'That's right, if you don't mind,' Mike said. 'I don't like leaving him all evening.'

'Fair enough, lad. Hey, what's all this?' Jed leaned forward, noticing the books and brochures on improved farming methods scattered about the table. He saw, too, the notepad beside them, crammed with written notes. 'You've been researching all this as well as repairing the cottage? When do you get time to sleep, Mike?'

Mike gave a dismissive laugh. 'Seriously, Jed, there's so much that could be done to the farm which would make it far more profitable. With a bit of shrewd investment you could easily make this the best dairy unit in the area.'

Jed shook his head slowly. 'But I'm not interested in huge profits. I'm happy to let the farm tick along and make us a reasonable living.'

'But, Jed, that won't be enough to guarantee a viable future,' Mike said urgently. 'If that's your attitude you could be left behind altogether. And you have your sons' livelihood to think of.'

'All this fancy talk's fine if money were no object.' Jed opened one of the books. 'I'm not saying I wouldn't like some of this fancy new equipment, but I've never thought it worth the outlay before. There are too many risks.'

'But it doesn't have to be like that,' Mike broke in enthusiastically. 'You know there are grants and schemes available? And not only home-grown ones. There are European grants, too. I'm telling you, with a little financial assistance and some sound advice, you could turn this place into a real goldmine, Jed. I've been doing my homework, getting some facts and figures together. Maybe you'd like to take a look sometime? See if it gives you any ideas?'

Jed rubbed his chin thoughtfully. He'd never given much thought to the matter, always believing improvements to be nothing but a costly headache. But if Mike was right, and it would be a legacy for his children, it might just be worth considering.

*  *  *

In the private wing of the mansion house at the holiday and leisure complex, all was quiet and still. Phil Scott stood before the mirror, straightening his tie and tugging his shirt cuffs. It was almost time to pick Kari up at her hotel and he felt like a teenager getting ready for a heavy date. The face in the mirror grinned back at him. 'It's a long time since you've felt this good, isn't it?' he said to his reflection.

He'd spent the day with Kari — a wonderful, exhilarating day, showing her around. He'd taken her on a guided tour of the holiday complex and leisure centre. Then they'd had lunch together in the restaurant before going horse-riding for the afternoon. She'd been impressed with the holiday complex and he knew her praise was genuine. Although he knew nothing about her, he could tell that she spoke her mind. And he'd enjoyed her company. She was bright, sparkling, and never at a loss for words.

His eyes glanced on a photograph on his dressing-table of his late wife,

Laura. He'd accepted Kari's praise for his leisure complex without a thought, yet it hadn't all been his idea. Laura had been his inspiration through all the years of planning, and together they'd dreamed of making a success of the holiday complex. In fact, it had been Laura's idea to get out of the London rat race and move to the Lake District.

Yet, tragically, she'd died before they'd had a chance to realise their dreams; before they'd had the children they'd planned. Laura had been so lovely, warm and intelligent, gentle and witty. How he wished she could have lived long enough to see all this. She'd left such a void in his life; an emptiness that he'd thought could never be filled.

After her death, he'd carried on with their plans, fervently wanting to fulfil her dreams; to create a living memorial to the woman he loved. And it had been quite a struggle, he had to admit. There had been times when he'd felt like packing it all in. Meetings had been held in the village hall, petitions handed

162

in, and he'd received sacks full of mail from far and wide, from people concerned that his plans would be carried out at the expense of much natural beauty.

Time and patience had won them over. He'd attended all their meetings, answered all their questions truthfully, and listened carefully and attentively to their worries and fears. He'd promised that not a single tree would be felled in the development of the complex. He'd kept his word and earned the admiration and respect of the local people.

He smiled ruefully. He'd made a major success of it, financially too, but there had never been anyone to share the triumph with — no other woman to compare with Laura. Until now.

He very much wanted tonight to be special too, for Kari as well as himself. Whatever her reasons for being here, whatever the reason behind the shadow of unhappiness that he'd glimpsed in her lovely eyes, it didn't make any difference to the way he was beginning to feel for her.

Kari Reynolds was special. She had to be to make him feel this way again after so long.

*  *  *

The dance was an annual event held in the village hall and was always well attended by the locals. And Mike was becoming very much part of the local scene himself, popular and well liked by all who knew him.

Kari had her own kind of magnetic appeal. The local people were fascinated by her, and speculation about the reasons for her sudden arrival in the village was rife.

Mike and Amy were among the early arrivals. Amy looked stunning in a simple dark green dress which showed off her creamy white skin. She seemed confident, at ease and perfectly happy, until Phil walked in with Kari on his arm.

Mike saw the sudden startled look on Amy's face, the two bright pink spots which appeared on her cheeks, and followed her gaze towards the door.

Kari, as ever, looked quite sensational, this time in a pale green dress which complemented perfectly the colour of her eyes. She walked confidently on high-heeled shoes and as she made her way across the floor, it seemed that everyone in the hall had turned to watch her. An interested silence descended. Phil, walking beside her, was aware of the attention she was attracting and was obviously proud to be escorting such a stunning young woman.

She was heading straight for Mike and Amy. They only had time to exchange horrified glances before she was standing right beside their table.

'Mike! Amy! How nice to see you,' Kari said pleasantly. Her smile was wide and it chilled Amy to the core. She would have preferred it if Kari had been cool and distant. At least she could have handled that.

'Hi, Kari.' Politely, Mike got to his feet. 'How're you doing?'

'Oh, Phil's been taking good care of me,' she said, casting a coy backward glance at Phil, who was hovering behind. 'We spent the day touring the area. He's a really nice guy.'

Amy tried to smile. Fear had frozen her face. Why was Kari suddenly being so nice and friendly? And what was she doing here at the dance?

'I had no idea this area was so beautiful,' Kari gushed. 'And to find Phil's leisure complex was simply a joy.'

'Well, I'm glad you're enjoying yourself, Kari.' Mike smiled warmly.

'Oh, I sure am!' She flashed a viperish smile at Amy. 'I have to tell you, it's really good to be here. And the fun hasn't even started yet.'

'Excuse me.' Phil intervened with a friendly smile. 'Hello Amy, Mike. Kari, I've got us a table over there,' he said, taking her arm.

'Excuse us,' Kari said. 'Perhaps we'll catch you later.'

'What's she doing here?' Amy whispered urgently as Phil led Kari off to the other side of the room.

'How should I know?' Mike shrugged as if he really didn't care. 'But I'm glad she's enjoying herself. Come on, Amy, forget about Kari for now. Let's just have a good time. Do you want to dance?'

Amy tried to forget her rival but it was impossible. Kari, in her eye-catching satin dress, kept slipping into view. Amy danced with Mike, sinking into the comfort of his arms, but each glimpse of Kari brought with it a disquieting fear that something none-too-pleasant was about to erupt.

Eventually, Amy became aware of Kari threading her way through the dancers towards them. 'Mike,' she said persuasively. 'How about a dance, baby? For old times' sake. Remember this song?'

Mike looked awkwardly at Amy.

'It's OK,' she whispered, forcing a smile.

'They played this song for us on the night we got engaged,' Kari told Amy.

167

'It's very special to us, isn't it, Mike?' Before he could answer, Kari pulled him onto the dance floor. For a second, Amy watched as Kari and Mike melted into the dancers on the floor, then she felt Phil Scott's hand on her arm.

'No need for us to be wallflowers.' He grinned. 'Would you like to dance, Amy?'

She was grateful to him for rescuing her and leading her onto the dance floor. He was a good dancer, and moved perfectly in time with the music.

'I didn't realise that you knew Kari so well,' she commented.

'I don't, but I'm hoping to get to know her much better.' He smiled boyishly as the music ended and they parted. 'Thank you.' He smiled down at Amy. 'Now, if you'll excuse me . . . ' Swiftly, he headed off to reclaim Kari, while Amy returned to her table to wait for Mike. The music started up again and she caught sight of him. She also saw Kari reaching out for him, slipping into his arms for another dance.

And Amy had no option but to watch. She wanted to look away, but her eyes were constantly drawn to the couple on the dance floor. They looked so right together that the doubts and insecurities Amy thought had died, came bubbling to the surface. Kari was smiling radiantly, laughing at everything Mike said, and he seemed to Amy equally entranced as he looked down at her.

'Amy! Hello, I thought it was you.'

Amy looked up and saw Carol, the receptionist from Phil Scott's holiday complex, smiling down at her.

'Oh, hi, Carol. How are you?' she asked glumly.

'I'm OK, thanks,' Carol answered as she sat down in Mike's empty chair. 'But you look a bit down. What's up? Not enjoying yourself? That friend of yours . . . Mike, isn't it? He seems to have hit it off with that American girl. She's a stunner, isn't she?'

'What?' Amy blinked.

'I told her this morning, up at the

leisure complex, that a fellow American would be here tonight. Aw, just look at them. They look good together, don't they? Like they were made for each other.' Carol smiled indulgently. 'Oh, crikey, I'd better be off, I can see my boyfriend looking for me. Bye, Amy. And cheer up — it might never happen.'

Mike loped back to the table to join her as soon as the music finished, smiling apologetically. 'Sorry about that,' he said, sitting down close beside her. 'She asked for another dance and I didn't want to be a jerk and refuse.'

'How considerate of you,' Amy replied coolly.

'Would you like to dance now, Amy? Or can I get you another drink?'

'I'm all right, thanks,' she said in a low voice. She could hardly bring herself to speak to him. Seeing Mike and Kari together like that had brought it home to her how fragile love could be. And Carol's remark about them looking so right together had just rubbed salt in the wound. Kari's being here was obviously no accident. She'd used Phil to get her here and it seemed that her ploy had worked. She more or less had Mike eating out of her hand.

'Amy?' Mike said. He was gazing at her with his warm, gentle eyes and she felt so near to tears that she had to look away. She knew she couldn't bear it if . . .

'Amy, what's wrong?' He stroked her bare arm, sending shivers down her spine. She pulled away from his touch.

'Amy?'

'It's nothing,' she lied, looking miserably at him.

'Let's get out of here,' he said urgently. She nodded and let him take her hand, leading her towards the open doors. Outside, the night air was fragrant and still, a sharp contrast to the noisy, stuffy atmosphere inside the hall.

Perhaps Mike realised that he belonged with Kari, too. Amy waited for him to say the words and admit he'd made a mistake. Perhaps he'd be using that air ticket his father sent him after all.

Mike took a deep breath. 'Hey, that's better! It was stuffy in there, wasn't it?'

'Yes,' she whispered.

'Oh, Amy.' He turned and took her hands in his. 'Tell me what's wrong, honey? You've been so quiet and distant all night. Surely it's not because I danced with Kari?'

Her silence told him it was.

'But why? It was only a dance. I only agreed because I didn't want to humiliate her more than I already have. You can understand that, can't you, Amy?'

'It isn't just that.' Tears sprang to her eyes. 'Oh, Mike, Kari's so beautiful. When I was watching you dancing together, it was like — like you were meant for each other. You look so right together. I can't compete with Kari, Mike. I can't think why you ever gave her up — not for someone like me.'

'Someone like you?'

She cast her eyes down and he stared at her for a moment. Then he tilted her chin and shook his head sadly when he saw the tears glistening on her cheeks.

'Oh, Amy, Amy,' he sighed, brushing them gently away. Then, reaching for her hand, he held it tightly in his own. Looking straight into her eyes, he murmured, 'I've told you before, I've never met anyone like you. Nobody, not even Kari, can hold a candle to you as far as I'm concerned. I love you. You're beautiful, and that beauty is inside you, too, Amy. You're warm, caring and loving, and I love everything about you. If I wanted Kari, do you really think I'd be here with you now? You're the only one for me. What I feel for Kari is, well, still friendship, I suppose. I don't want to hurt her, but I don't love her, not in the real sense of the word; not the way I love you. Now do you believe me?' he whispered.

All those terrifying doubts and fears suddenly vanished, as if they'd been spirited away. All that was left was Amy and Mike and the beautiful night. He kissed her then and she moved into his arms, feeling that it was right, knowing she belonged.

'Go with your heart. Trust your feelings, but be sure of them,' her mother had said. Well, now she was sure. She'd never been more sure of anything in her life.

As he brushed her tears away, he saw she was smiling.

'Mike.' She held his hands and looked up, eyes shining, into his.

'Yes,' he whispered.

'Michael Carter,' she said demurely, 'will you marry me?'

# 7

Warm air, pulsating music and laughter wafted into their faces as Amy and Mike went back into the dance hall. His arm was draped comfortably around her shoulders and both were glowing with happiness and love for each other.

Sam, who had been doing a unique and very spirited impression of Patrick Swayze while his long-suffering wife, Kate, looked on, caught sight of them and waved.

Amy looked happily up at Mike and kissed him lightly.

'I'll just phone Mum and Dad,' she whispered and slipped away, dissolving into a sea of bodies and leaving Mike feeling quite lost without her.

'I'll bet you don't have knockout dos like this in America!' Sam, who'd had a few, remarked, slapping Mike affection-ately on the shoulder. 'Let's have another drink, lad.'

Grinning, Mike replied, 'Oh, I don't know about that, Sam. We Americans know how to have a good time, too, you know. Without all that beer,' he added with a grin.

'Aw, c'mon, lad, you can surely join me in a little drink.'

'No way, Sam. Besides,' he grinned, 'I reckon my fiancée wouldn't approve of my getting drunk tonight of all nights.'

'Your fiancée?'

'That's right, Sam! I want you to be the first to know that Amy and I are to be married. She's calling her mom with the good news right now.'

'Well, that's smashing news, lad. Congratulations.' Sam slapped Mike on the back again and then, to Mike's surprise, turned and disappeared into the throng of dancers.

The music came to an abrupt halt as Sam appeared on the stage and started fiddling with the microphone. Mike looked on interestedly. A hush came down on the packed hall as everyone turned in anticipation towards the stage, wondering why the music had suddenly stopped.

'Good evening!' Sam bellowed into the mike.

From a few yards away, Kate exchanged a resigned look with Mike.

'Sorry to interrupt the dancing,' Sam went on, responding to the buzz of interest that rippled through the dancers. 'But when I tell you why, you'll all be glad, I'm sure.'

'What's going on?' Amy appeared at Mike's side and slipped her hand into his. Before Mike could answer, a slightly unsteady Sam was speaking again to the assembly.

'You all know our Amy Palmer, and many of you have come to know Mike Carter, the American lad who's helping out up at their farm. Well, it gives me great pleasure to announce that this evening they've just become engaged!'

The applause was deafening. People were cheering and clapping and those closest to Amy and Mike were shouting their congratulations even as the band struck up their rendition of 'Congratulations'. Almost at once, Mike and Amy were surrounded by people all offering their best wishes. Suddenly, it was their evening and everyone wanted to share in their happiness.

There were tears in Amy's eyes at such a warm response to Sam's announcement. She had no idea so many people cared and had taken Mike to their hearts.

★　★　★

Kari, who had been dancing with Phil when the music had stopped abruptly, felt numb as people pushed past her to get to Amy and Mike.

Phil stood beside her, one hand resting lightly on her waist. They made a very handsome couple, but there was only one couple in whom Kari was interested. She just couldn't believe what she'd heard. The band were still hammering out 'Congratulations' and every drum beat, every lively note, drove the pain deeper and deeper. How could he? How could he be so cruel?

She felt sick and dizzy but, worst of all, betrayed. When she'd danced with Mike earlier, she'd really felt that there was still something there. Yet all the time, he'd been planning this.

'Aw, that's great news.' Phil was clapping and smiling happily. 'They make a really nice couple, don't they?'

She'd gone deathly white and her eyes suddenly looked very unhappy.

'Kari? Are you all right? What's wrong?'

She hardly trusted herself to speak, scared that if she opened her mouth all the pain and bitterness would come gushing out in an unstoppable stream. 'Would you take me back to my hotel, Phil, please?' she whispered at last, her voice small and shaky.

'Why? What's wrong?' he repeated. 'Are you ill, Kari?'

She didn't answer him, but pushed her way blindly to the door. He followed close behind. Outside in the foyer, he helped her on with her coat. His hands brushed against her bare arms.

'You're cold, Kari,' he said, putting an arm around her.

She stiffened at his touch. Then she looked up at him and he couldn't help thinking how beautiful she was. Yet, at that moment, he'd never seen anyone look so miserable. Her lovely eyes were full of pain.

'Don't fuss, Phil,' she said, sounding more like herself. 'I'm OK. I just want to go back to my hotel and get some rest. I guess I'm tired.'

'Right,' he said, still looking anxious. 'If that's what you want, Kari.'

\* \* \*

Kari stood in her hotel room and heard the roar of Phil's car as he sped off, back to the dance. Poor Phil. He'd seemed so bewildered when she'd said goodnight and rushed off to her room without even thanking him properly.

She was shaking all over and fighting

to hold back the tears.

She mustn't go to pieces now.

She looked down at her engagement ring, the ring Mike had placed on her finger when he'd asked her to marry him. The diamonds sparkled in a huge cluster. She remembered how he'd slipped it onto her finger, then kissed it, all the while looking deep into her eyes. She could see his eyes so clearly in her mind — his loving eyes, loving her.

The shaking stopped. She was being silly. Mike did love her! He always had and he always would. Picking up a framed photograph of him that she kept beside her bed, she looked into his eyes.

'The odds may be well and truly stacked against me, Mike,' she whispered. 'But I'm not about to let you go without a fight!'

* * *

Some time had passed since the announcement of Mike and Amy's engagement. It was harvest time and an especially busy period for Jed. He'd had to take on extra hands. Looking at him, no one would ever have guessed how close he'd come to dying so recently. He felt revitalised. He'd taken on a new lease of life and was working with even more drive and enthusiasm.

Even he was amazed at how quickly things had changed on the farm. With Mike's help, he'd put forward his plans for improving the farm. He'd had a new cowshed built for the dairy herd, now that it had doubled in size. He had adopted new working methods and labour-saving devices which, he'd been assured, would cut costs in the long run. He was looking to a future of large profits and a farm of which he could be proud.

And, of course, Mike's expertise was behind it all. It was Mike who had encouraged him; Mike who had looked into the grants and loans available; and it was Mike who had been there to advise him on the best long-term buys, negotiating deals with big companies over the supply of new equipment.

He was doing it for his family, Jed told himself. If it all went to plan, it would be a substantial inheritance to pass on. He felt more at ease in his mind now about the future.

'Busy?' Mike strolled across the yard to where Jed had been standing deep in thought.

'I was just thinking,' Jed remarked, 'how much this place has changed in such a short time. It takes a bit of getting used to.'

'You've no regrets though, Jed?'

'None, lad. I've bought in some grand beasts for the dairy herd, fresh pedigree stock. I'm going to have the finest dairy herd in the northwest, you mark my words.'

'You're pretty fond of these animals of yours, aren't you, Jed?' Mike said.

'Ay, I am that. I can't imagine farming without them.' Jed sighed. 'There's not much room for sentiment in this business, Mike, but I don't mind admitting, you can't help getting attached to the livestock — especially when you've raised most of the original herd yourself, as I have.'

Mike nodded. He knew well enough how Jed loved his animals — from the devoted Labrador, Bracken, to that crotchety old sheep that lived in a pen on its own.

'You're not thinking of walking out on us now, are you, Mike?' Jed asked, only half-joking. 'I'm doing this for my lads and Amy's sister Joanna and the two of you. Oh, and for the grandchildren I'm hoping will come along some day.'

'Don't worry.' Mike smiled and gently squeezed his future father-in-law's arm. 'This is my home now. I'm not going anywhere.'

'Well, I'm glad to hear that,' Jed sighed.

'Come on,' Mike said with a wide smile. 'Sheila sent me out here to tell you lunch is nearly ready. She'll tan both our hides if she sees us gossiping.'

Laughing, the two men walked off towards the farmhouse.

*   *   *

Phil Scott sat alone at a window table
in the lounge bar of his hotel, from
where he had an uninterrupted view of
the lake and mountains beyond. Trees
were beginning to turn and shed their
leaves, everything was bathed in a
mellow golden glow, and the view was
even more spectacular.

He sensed Kari's presence and turned
in time to see her walking towards him.
He stood up and kissed her cheek in
greeting. 'I've ordered you a drink,' he
said softly. 'Kari, you look fabulous.'

'Thanks.' She gave a brief, preoccupied smile and sat down opposite Phil.

'Kari, we've had a great time these
past few weeks, haven't we?' Phil
murmured, putting his hand over hers.
She flinched at his touch, but didn't
withdraw her hand.

'Sure.' Her smile wavered slightly and
he was quick to notice it. 'But . . . '

'But?'

'Look, Phil,' she said evenly, 'I should

have explained all this before now. My reason for staying here is simple — Mike Carter.'

'Mike? But he's . . . '

'You don't have to tell me,' she said quickly and held out her hand, showing him the sparkling diamond ring. 'Didn't you wonder about this?' she asked.

He nodded. Of course he'd noticed the fabulous, expensive ring, but as she'd never mentioned a man by name, he hadn't thought too much about it. He'd assumed it was a symbol of the past rather than a sign of something ongoing.

'Mike Carter put it on my finger,' she said flatly.

Phil gasped, unable to hide his shock.

'We grew up together,' she began. 'Then as we got older, our friendship . . . ' She hesitated. 'Turned to love — real love, Phil, not this ludicrous infatuation he feels for Amy Palmer.' She stopped for a moment, then continued bleakly, 'We'd have been married by now if he hadn't come to England and met her.

He was supposed to spend a few days here at most, but he met her and that was it.'

'He must be crazy,' Phil muttered, but she didn't seem to hear him.

'But I'm not going to give up on him, Phil. I love him and I know that, deep down, he loves me. This thing with Amy Palmer is just a passing fancy. I know it is, and sooner or later he will too. How can he be truly in love with someone he's known for such a short time? It just isn't possible.'

Phil bit back his reply. On the contrary, he felt like saying, it was perfectly possible to fall in love with someone quickly and devastatingly. In fact, he knew better than anyone just how possible it was.

'So where does that leave us, Kari?' he asked softly.

'There is no 'us', Phil,' she said gently, her beautiful eyes full of compassion. 'I'm sorry if I've led you to believe otherwise.' Her voice trailed off distractedly. 'I'm very fond of you, Phil.

187

You're a nice guy and you've been a really good friend since I got over here. But you're not Mike. If things had been different, if I wasn't still in love with Mike, then maybe it could have been the start of something, but I can't let you think there could be anything between us. It just wouldn't be fair.'

This was the last thing Phil had expected to hear, but he tried not to let his feelings show.

'Maybe we should just leave it now,' she murmured, drawing her hand away from his.

'Leave it?' Phil looked up sharply. He admired her strength and resolve. But he was a fighter, too. He had dreams and he'd always been prepared to go to any lengths to fulfil them. Just as Kari wasn't about to give up on Mike, he wasn't going to let her go so easily. 'Can't we be friends?' he said persuasively. 'We enjoy being together. We get along well. It'd be a shame to let all that go.'

'You're not mad at me?' She smiled

almost shyly and he felt his heart flip over inside him.

'No, of course I'm not mad,' he replied softly. How could he ever be mad at her? 'We'll still see each other now and then, won't we, Kari?'

'As friends.' She smiled again. 'Just as friends.'

'Of course,' he agreed sadly.

★ ★ ★

Sam looked over the outside of the pretty little cottage and nodded his approval. 'Ay, you've made a right difference to the old place, Mike,' he complimented him. 'When I first met you in the Ram's Head, I'd never have thought you'd got it in you, but you've surprised us all.' He caught the look which passed between Amy and Mike and smiled to himself. 'Where is he then?' He rubbed his hands together.

'Oh, the pup? He's called Cosby.' Mike grinned and twisted his key in the front door of the cottage.

At once, Cosby bounded out, much bigger now, all great big feet and thumping tail, greeting them all ecstatically.

'Ah, now.' Sam smiled. 'You're letting him walk all over you. You've got to show them who's boss right from the start. I've had plenty of experience with Labs. They'll soon spot you for a pushover if you let 'em.'

Amy, with a quirky smile, said, 'Sam's something of an expert when it comes to handling dogs.'

'I see.' Mike's mouth twitched. 'Sam seems to be an authority on a lot of things.'

'Ay,' Sam agreed. 'There's not much I don't know about dogs, women or rabbits!'

'In that order?' Mike asked with a wink at Amy.

'In any order, lad!'

'Well, he's bright and willing to please,' Mike said. 'Training him when the time comes should be no problem.'

Sam pushed his pipe between his

teeth and rocked back on his heels. 'You can't start 'em too young, that's what I say. I'll show you.' Sam called the pup to him and Cosby immediately started nipping madly at Sam's boot laces. 'No!' Sam said to the pup. 'Firm, but kind, you see,' he added knowingly to Mike. 'Sit!'

Cosby ignored Sam's command and started attacking his boot laces again.

'No.' Sam prized Cosby's jaws from the soggy laces and lifted him into his arms. The pup began to wriggle and lick his face, bringing gales of laughter from Sam.

'Oh, it's no good.' He guffawed. 'I haven't the time or the patience.' He shrugged. 'He's a fine pup, Mike, but I don't envy you trying to train him. He's right strong-willed, that one. No!' Sam said again and waved his finger at the pup. This time Cosby sat back clumsily, one ear flopped over his head, looking at Sam with big brown eyes that were at once cheeky and appealing.

'Good boy.' Sam laughed. 'Did you

see that? He knows what's what. That he does.'

The pup wagged his tail and rolled on to his back, kicking his legs in the air gleefully.

'Yep.' Mike laughed, clapping his hand on Sam's shoulder. 'I reckon he does.'

\* \* \*

'Bad news, darling?' Barbara Carter couldn't keep the anxiety from her voice as she walked into the spacious hall of their mansion, just as her husband was putting down the telephone receiver. His troubled look suggested it was something to do with that wayward son of theirs.

'Things can't go on as they are,' Michael said, turning to face her, fire in his eyes. 'He's messed up everything.'

'I take it you mean Mike,' she said softly.

'Of course I mean Mike! Who else? It's not just that he's let us all down, hurt Kari and gone and got himself engaged to this English girl. It's the business I'm worried about. Our interests in Britain are suffering because of him. He's opted out. I left him to it, thinking he'd come to his senses, but he hasn't. He's still carrying on with this ridiculous charade. I should have gone to England myself right at the start instead of letting him make his own decisions. Look at the mess he's got us all into now. I'm worn out.'

'Simmer down, darling,' Barbara said soothingly. 'You'll make yourself ill if you go on like this.'

'OK, OK,' he replied irritably. 'But I'm through with all of this, Barbara. As soon as I've gotten things settled here, we're going to England to sort this out once and for all.'

Barbara couldn't hide her pleasure at the news. 'We're going to see Mike?' she said happily. 'Oh, darling, I'm so glad.' She was finding this enforced estrangement from her son very painful and hard to deal with, and she was so pleased to know that she'd be seeing him again at last. She'd been dismayed when Michael had frozen all Mike Junior's money and refused to remain in contact.

But now, perhaps, there could be a reconciliation.

'I'm going to talk some sense into that boy if it's the last thing I do,' Michael said vehemently, and Barbara felt glad she was going along too to keep the peace between the two most important men in her life.

'Wh-when are we going?' she said, biting her lip.

'As soon as I can arrange it,' he replied. 'I don't intend to leave it a moment longer than I have to.'

\* \* \*

Jed came in from the byre and found his wife waiting in the kitchen for him. There wasn't much he could hide from Sheila. She knew him better than he knew himself. He sat down at the table and put his head in his hands.

'Jed?' Sheila sat down beside him.

All day he'd been telling her that everything was all right, knowing she didn't believe him. He'd been putting off calling out the vet, as if by delaying contacting him, he could stop it all from happening.

'Will you call Edward, love?' he asked softly. 'And ask him to come.'

Sheila nodded. 'It's late, Jed. Couldn't it wait until morning?'

'You know it can't,' he replied. 'I've put it off long enough. We need him now. I'll wait for him in the byre. You stay in the house, love.'

Jed stood in the yard, looking up at the clear night sky spotted with twinkling stars. It was a beautiful night, clear and calm. He shivered, despite the fact that it was warm inside his padded jacket.

He heard one of the cows lowing and shivered again. Bracken came up beside him and nuzzled his hand, pushing her cold wet nose into his palm, begging to be stroked. The dog could sense his sadness and was trying to comfort him in the only way she knew how.

He stroked her velvet soft head and felt his throat constricting painfully. It was only a couple of days since he'd stood in the yard with Mike, speaking proudly about his plans for the future.

What future?

It was 20 minutes before he heard a car engine coming down the rough track towards the farm.

He could still be wrong, he told himself as a Land Rover pitched into the yard.

'Sheila said it was urgent.' Edward Smethurst, the vet, jumped out of the car, grabbing his bag. 'I came straight over.'

'In the byre,' Jed said, his voice low and flat.

'I heard you'd bought in some new stock recently, Jed?'

Jed turned to look at the young vet, his eyes misty. 'Ay,' he muttered, 'and I'm beginning to think that was the biggest mistake of my life.'

'Why don't you wait out here?' the vet said kindly. 'I'll take a look.'

Jed nodded. He didn't want to be there. He didn't want any of this to be happening. He looked over his shoulder and saw Sheila at the window of the farmhouse, looking out anxiously, holding the curtain aside. He ought to go and speak to her, but he couldn't face her yet.

When he turned again, the vet was coming out of the byre. He couldn't see his face clearly in the darkness.

'You knew, didn't you, Jed?' he said quietly.

Jed nodded. He'd sensed hours ago what was wrong with the beasts. 'I was praying it wasn't.'

'Sorry, Jed.' Edward's shoulders sagged as he spoke. 'I know I don't have to tell you how serious foot and mouth disease is. Frankly, it couldn't be worse.'

# 8

It had only been days, but it seemed like weeks because of the eerie silence that hung over the place now. Jed stood by the kitchen window, looking out at the empty farmyard. Even the old sheep that he had kept as a family pet had gone.

He shuddered, remembering in graphic detail those horrific few hours: the arrival of the men from the ministry, the police cordons, the signs going up on the gate. Then, finally, the arrival of the slaughter men.

They'd told Jed it would be better to keep out of the way, but how could he? There was no room for sentiment in farming — no one knew that better than him — but, by heaven, he'd been fond of those beasts. They'd been his whole working life. He felt an aching emptiness now that he didn't know how to deal with. He felt a lone tear trickle down his cheek. Fiercely, he brushed it away.

Sheila had been watching him, standing there by the kitchen window, knuckles white as he gripped the window-sill, torturing himself. Foot and mouth. Three stark words which struck terror into the heart of the farming community.

There had been two cases reported from other farms, but the authorities reckoned they'd managed to contain it. Still, everyone would have to be vigilant.

Now the farm was in quarantine, the beasts all destroyed and the carcasses burned. Bracken, putting on weight now that her pups had gone, padded up to Jed and nuzzled his leg, whining softly when she got no response.

He'd locked everything and everyone out, shutting himself away with his grief. Sheila went over to him and made him turn to face her, away from the empty yard outside.

'Jed, you'll have to try to snap out of this. We've been through bad times before. Maybe not this bad, but we'll come out of this, too. It won't be easy. We both know that, but together we'll see this through, love.'

He sighed. 'Ay, lass, I know that. It's just so quiet out there,' he said softly, putting an arm around her. He looked at his wife then and hated himself for bringing all this worry on her. He forced a smile.

'What would I do without you?' he said gently, brushing her cheek with his big rough hand. 'But it's not just the herd, Sheila.' He gave her an anguished look. 'It's the thought of all that money I borrowed for the rebuilding and restocking. How am I ever going to repay that now?' He shrugged hopelessly, moving away from her then, towards the back door.

'Where are you going, Jed?' she asked fretfully.

'To the milking shed,' he said evenly, putting up his hands to silence the inevitable protest that rose to her lips. 'I have to say goodbye in my own way, love. Grant me that.'

His feet made no sound as he crossed the yard. As he opened the door to the milking shed, Jed breathed in and smelled not the warm, familiar smell of beasts and milk and hay, but the astringent, sharp tang of disinfectant.

Moving along the stalls, he paused at each one to touch the name painted there. Each beast had to be named for registration. Cowslip, Buttercup, Bluebell, Daisy, Meadowsweet . . .

'Meadowsweet.' He said the name aloud. Daft name for a cow, but she was sweetest, the gentlest, least temperamental beast he'd ever known. High milk yield, too, and never any bother at calving time.

'God, why did it have to happen?' he muttered.

He stopped at a stall which bore no name, unaware of two slender shadows falling down the centre of the shed as Amy and Mike stood watching him uneasily from the shaded doorway.

One of the new beasts, a top-quality animal. He'd known she was going to be special the minute he'd set eyes on her. A special creature like that needed a special name. That was why he hadn't got round to giving her one, and now it was too late.

He sighed a long, shuddering sigh.

Standing in the doorway, Mike felt Amy's nails dig into his arm. When he looked down at her, she was pale and trembling. She'd never seen her father like this before, so dispirited, so low. These past few days, working on the farm had been like living through a nightmare. Everyone was still numb from the catastrophe.

Hearing a movement at the doorway, Jed came outside, blinking in the sunlight. He didn't seem surprised to see Amy and Mike standing there.

'Dad . . . ' Amy began, but something about her father's distracted manner warned her not to probe. She understood. A sympathetic word spoken now could easily cause him even greater torment.

It was Mike who broke the ensuing silence. 'I'm really sorry, Jed,' he said wretchedly. 'This is all my fault. If I hadn't interfered, if I'd kept out of your business . . . I should never have talked you into making all those improvements. And I can't do a damn thing to help you out of it.' He ran his hands through his hair in frustration. 'I can't get my hands on my own money, would you believe.' He was pacing up and down in anguish and he only stopped when Jed reached out and placed his work-roughened hand on the younger man's strong, tanned arm.

'Now that'll do, lad. Calm down. You didn't force me to borrow money and make the changes. No one twisted my arm. I made my own decisions; I signed on the dotted line.'

Mike made himself look at Jed.

'Start blaming people and God only knows where it'll end. As for the foot and mouth, well, something like that can happen any time, lad, anywhere. We're all powerless to stop it once it strikes. So think on, Mike. It's not your fault or anyone else's.' He spoke the words with real conviction and smiled wearily at Mike, then at Amy.

Amy was filled with sadness for what her father must be going through and for the loss of all those animals.

'What are you going to do?' Mike asked.

Jed shrugged. 'I'll go and have a word with the bank manager first of all. He might let me borrow more money, but I know well enough you can't borrow yourself out of debt. If he turns me down, I'll have no option but to . . . ' He broke off, not wanting to spell it out. But he hadn't been quick enough, for he caught Amy's horrified look and knew that she realised what he'd been going to say. 'Better go on in for your supper, you two,' he said quickly. 'I'll just shut everything up here and I'll be along in a moment.'

Amy wanted to say something, but

Mike had hold of her arm and was propelling her towards the farmhouse. 'Not now, Amy,' he said. 'He needs another few moments on his own.'

Amy shook her arm free and rubbed angrily at the tears that had sprung to her eyes. 'I'm not so sure. Have you forgotten how ill he was just a few weeks ago?'

'No, I haven't forgotten,' Mike whispered.

They hesitated outside the door, both of them suffering unspoken agonies.

'The bank isn't going to lend him any more money,' Amy said dully. 'You know it and I know it and I think Dad knows it, too.'

Mike nodded slowly, then pushed the door open and waited for Amy to go inside. The kitchen was deserted and Amy set about laying the table, banging knives and forks down haphazardly. Mike watched her for a moment, puzzled. He knew she was upset, but today there was something more than the fate of the farm that was bothering her.

She turned, caught him watching her and her face blazed red. Hoping to see her smile, he said the first thing that came into his head, intending it to take her mind off what was happening and perhaps bring her out of the doldrums. 'Have you given any more thought to the wedding, sweetheart?' he asked softly. 'We ought to set a date, don't you think? Give everyone something to look forward to?' He smiled his wide, open smile that normally melted Amy's heart.

'Wedding!' The colour in Amy's cheeks burned deeper. 'All this has happened and you expect me to think about weddings? Take a good look around you, Mike, because I don't think you really know what's going on here. My dad's whole life is collapsing around him. Have you any idea of the dire straits we're in now? And it's your fault!' Her voice rose shrilly.

'Amy, I just thought . . . ' He stepped towards her, his eyes pleading, but she ducked away from him, deliberately avoiding any contact.

'Everything was all right until you came,' she went on accusingly. 'You came here and turned everything upside-down. My life, too. I don't know anything about you, Mike. I don't know you at all. How can we be thinking about marriage when we hardly know each other? How can we even contemplate a future together, when you've destroyed my parents' past, and their future?'

'Amy, please.' Mike's face had paled until he looked ashen. He was stricken by her outburst, unable to defend himself because, deep down, he couldn't deny she was right.

But he loved her. He couldn't bear the thought of losing her now, no matter what.

'Don't come near me,' she cried. 'Sometimes I wish I'd never set eyes on you, Mike. I wish you'd never come here. If you hadn't, Dad wouldn't be in this mess now. We wouldn't be facing losing everything we've got.'

'Listen, Amy,' Mike said miserably,

reaching out, wishing there was some way of getting through to her. 'I love you. We'll get round this. We'll talk it all out. Things probably seem worse than they really are right now.'

She pushed him away. Then, as he watched helplessly, she began to wrench at the engagement ring he'd placed so recently on her finger.

'No,' he whispered. 'No! Don't do that. Amy, please . . . '

She struggled with it, pulled it off and slapped it down on the table, sending cutlery spilling to the floor with a clatter and looking at Mike with grey eyes that blazed.

For a moment, they just stared at each other, neither of them quite believing what had just happened. Then, with an anguished wail, Amy fled from the room, rushing upstairs to her bedroom. She slammed the door behind her and threw herself on to the bed.

Where would this nightmare end? She sobbed, her tears soaking the pillow, her throat aching. Why had she turned on Mike? How could she, when she loved him so much? And why did she have to say such horrid, cruel things to him? He already blamed himself for what had happened and she'd just driven more nails into the coffin of his guilt. She realised the bitter irony of what she'd said as her words came back to torment her now.

'Dad wouldn't be in this fix now.' Of course he wouldn't. If Mike hadn't come when he did, her father wouldn't be alive.

'Oh, Mike.' She sobbed heartbrokenly. 'Why has it all gone so terribly wrong?'

\* \* \*

It was the first time the two families had got together since all the trouble began. The Reynoldses and the Carters had spoken on the phone and Barbara had been to see Kari's mother a couple of times in an attempt to mollify her, but this was the big one.

'I'm just so worried about Kari,'

Christine Reynolds confessed, her large eyes, grey-green like her daughter's, shimmering with unshed tears. 'I know she's tough and smart, but underneath, she's still just a young girl, with a normal girl's hopes and dreams. She calls regularly, but reading between the lines, I figure things aren't going too well.'

Here, Larry Reynolds chipped in. He was a big, bluff, warm-hearted man. 'Seems to me,' he drawled, 'we don't have too much idea what's going on. Our little girl's all alone over there in England, and Christine and I are worried about her.' He shrugged helplessly.

Michael Carter Senior placed another drink in Christine Reynolds's trembling hands. If his son could only see the repercussions of his selfish actions, he thought angrily. He'd not only broken Kari's heart, but caused her parents and themselves untold anguish, too. Goodness only knew what kind of a mess he was making of this new girl's life; the one he professed to love so much and

had been prepared to sacrifice everything for.

'Don't worry, folks,' he said, more
vehemently than he'd intended. 'Mike's
going to be made to face the conse-
quences of his actions. We love Kari as
if she were our own daughter and, as far
as I'm concerned, the sooner we can
get over to England and sort out this
mess, the better. Kari isn't going to
have to fight this thing on her own
much longer.'

'Darling, we still haven't heard
Mike's side of the story,' Barbara
pointed out, with an apologetic look at
the Reynoldses. 'Perhaps if he's really
discovered that he doesn't love Kari,
he's done the right thing by calling the
wedding off?'

Her husband glared at her for a
moment in disbelief. 'How can you say
that, Barbara? Of course he loves her.
Kari's a tremendous girl. One in a
million. And even if it were true, the
way he's gone about things is unforgiv-
able.'

'But he's still our son!' Barbara stood up, clenched her fists and fought back the tears. Mike was their only son and she loved him and feared a deepening rift between them. How could she live with that?

'Yes, I know that,' Michael said, a little less angrily. 'But it's time for all this nonsense to stop.'

The Reynoldses looked up at him anxiously as he paced the floor. 'Barbara and I are going to England immediately to sort this out once and for all. I'm just about to call Kari to let her know when we'll be arriving. She'll be there to meet us at the airport,' he told them. 'Like I said, Kari won't be fighting this on her own much longer.' He folded his arms across his chest and glowered at his wife.

Barbara managed to hide a smile. She couldn't wait to see her son again and to meet this Amy with whom he had become so infatuated.

★　★　★

Kari walked along the English country lane and glanced up. The fields were empty now. All the sheep had gone. She had already passed by one farm which was in quarantine, and the desolate air about it had made her shudder.

But she hadn't come out for this walk to consider the plight of local farmers. She was more concerned with Mike.

She smiled wryly. Her plans had gone terribly wrong. She'd arrived here thinking that her presence was all it would take to have Mike running to heel. How wrong she'd been. How she'd misjudged him and the situation.

She looked up again and, this time, saw Amy Carter in one of the fields with her dog trotting along beside her.

'Hi,' she called out, knowing that to walk past with her nose in the air ignoring Amy would have been childish and silly.

Amy turned and came down to the low wall. She looked really jaded, Kari noted, which was hardly surprising, considering what she'd been through lately.

'Hello, Kari,' Amy said uncertainly.

'It must be hard,' Kari said, thinking she must be the last person Amy wanted to bump into. 'I'm sorry about what's happened. It must be heart-breaking for all of you.'

Amy looked surprised. Kari had meant every word and there was genuine sympathy in her eyes. 'Yes,' she whispered. 'It is. We just don't know what's going to happen.'

'You're talking as if it's all over,' Kari ventured. 'Surely your father was insured?'

'Yes and no.' Amy smiled thinly. 'With all the changes that were happening, Dad only changed his insurers so that the new buildings would be covered. What he didn't realise was that the herd itself wasn't covered, and as he'd cancelled the old insurance . . . ' She shrugged. 'Even our original herd was uninsured. It was a tragic oversight — some might even say stupid — but Dad's a farmer, not a businessman, not really. He knows all there is to know about the animals, but paperwork's another story.'

'How awful.' Kari shook her head. 'I just wish I knew how to help.'

Amy looked up sharply and saw that Kari meant it. For a few moments the two of them stood with the wall between them, both of them aware that friendship might even have been possible if it were not for one singularly important stumbling block.

'How's Mike doing?' Kari asked the question lightly and was taken aback to see the unhappiness in Amy's eyes. Tears welled up in her eyes as she looked levelly at Kari.

'Mike? What can I say, Kari? I thought you might have heard by now.'

'Heard what?' Kari was aware of her heart thumping painfully.

'You've won, Kari. Mike and I are finished. I've given him back his ring.' Amy's voice was flat. Kari couldn't speak. The words she had longed to hear meant nothing. Not now. Perhaps it was seeing Amy's distress that touched her heart.

Whatever it was, she didn't feel the way she thought she should.

By the time she'd regained her senses, Amy had turned around and was walking back up the hill. There was a defeated slump to her shoulders; and even the dog, ambling at her side, seemed listless and out of sorts.

Kari watched them go, waiting for the elation to hit her, but it didn't happen. Inside, all she felt was a hollow sense of victory, in which there was no pleasure. Confused by her feelings, she turned around so she didn't have to watch Amy walking away and looked back down the long, meandering path to the village.

So it was over between them. Wasn't it what she had always hoped for? Expected even?

She set off at a brisk pace back down the hill, oblivious, for once, to her spectacular surroundings.

★　★　★

216

After an emotional reunion at the airport, Kari drove the Carters in her hired car back to the hotel, where she'd managed to book them a suite, now that the main summer rush was coming to an end. She hadn't yet told them about the latest developments; but now that there were just the three of them in the suite, it was time to talk.

'You're looking well, Kari,' Barbara Carter said, unable to keep the surprise out of her voice. 'We thought . . . '

'I'm fine,' Kari said quickly. She glanced at Michael Senior and looked quickly away. He looked like a man ready to do battle.

'Where's Mike?' he demanded impatiently. 'I don't want to waste any time.'

'You need to get over this jet-lag first, dear,' Barbara fussed, casting Kari a long-suffering look and hoping to put off the moment when father and son came face-to-face.

'Jet-lag! That's for the tourists. I came here to see my son, and by heck . . . '

'Not yet,' Kari said softly. 'I want to

217

talk to you first. There are certain things you should be aware of before you say or do anything.'

'What's with this kid gloves stuff?' he demanded. 'What's wrong with you, Kari? I thought you wanted this thing sorted out as much as I did.'

'Sit down, Michael,' Barbara said wearily. 'Let's hear what Kari has to say first.'

Kari looked unhappily from one to the other. 'Well, first of all, it's over between Mike and Amy. They've called off their engagement.'

'Terrific!' Michael smiled. 'That's good news, Kari, real good news. Looks like he's come to his senses at long last.'

'It's not as simple as that,' Kari said slowly. 'I'm pretty sure now that I could get Mike back just like that.' She clicked her fingers. 'There's been an outbreak of foot and mouth disease here and it's struck the Palmers' farm. They've lost just about everything and it seems that Mike and Amy's relationship has foundered under the strain of it all.'

'How awful for them,' Barbara said softly. 'About the farm, I mean. But I'm as relieved as you are about the romance being over.'

Michael no longer looked angry. He looked relieved and concerned at the same time. 'It's tragic when a man loses everything,' he said with feeling. 'It seems Mike has brought nothing but bad luck to the Palmers.'

'You could be right,' Kari said. 'Look, so much has happened here in the past few days and, well, I've been doing a lot of thinking. I've reached a decision and I'm going to need your help.'

Michael looked at her, the admiration clear in his eyes. He reached out and held his wife's hand. They were all in this together, he and Barbara and Kari. Whatever it took to get Mike back on the straight and narrow, it would be done together.

'Go ahead, Kari,' he said. 'We'll do whatever we can to help you get Mike back. Just fire away, honey. We're all ears.'

'Right, this is what I had in mind . . . '

# 9

Kari looked affectionately at the faces of the couple who were to have been her parents-in-law. She loved them dearly and whatever happened, nothing would ever change how she felt about them. They were both watching her closely now, waiting to hear what she had to say. She'd been thinking about this meeting for days, but now that the moment was here she wasn't quite sure where or how to begin.

'I'm sorry,' she said at last, apologising for taking so long to get started. 'I had it all rehearsed, what I was going to say to you, but I guess I've forgotten the words. It's not easy for me to say this and I guess it's going to be even harder for you to understand. I don't quite understand myself, except that what's happened has happened . . . and I can't turn things around, however much I'd like to.'

'Hold on,' Michael interrupted. 'I thought you said you could get Mike back. Are you saying you can't? Is he still giving you a hard time?'

'No. I just, I never thought I'd hear myself say this, but I truly believe that Amy is the right girl for Mike.' She looked earnestly from one to the other. 'Before you say anything, please hear me out. I've watched them together over the past few weeks and though it hurts me to admit it, no one has ever looked more right as a couple than those two do.'

'Oh, Kari, sweetheart, how awful for you,' Barbara breathed, her heart going out to this lovely girl whom she would have been proud to call her daughter-in-law. 'It must have been a nightmare for you.'

'Darn that stupid boy!' Michael's exasperation made his cheeks turn red.

'Take it easy, honey,' Barbara said soothingly. 'Remember your blood pressure. Anyway, Kari hasn't finished yet. Go on, dear.'

'I did everything I could think of to make Mike see sense . . . well, sense as I saw it. But now I know he loves her, and she loves him. I saw her just after they broke up and she looked devastated. She seemed even more shattered than I was when Mike broke it off with me. I guess what I'm trying to say is what Mike has been trying to make me see all this time. I do still love him, but more as a friend. Because we grew up together, everyone just kind of assumed we'd get married. Mike's right, it would never have worked. Our love had become a habit. I can see that now.' Her voice wavered slightly. 'And getting him back became a matter of saving face. It's time for me to bow out with what's left of my self-esteem, I guess.'

'Well,' Michael Senior remarked with a sigh, 'I've heard it all now. He's even got you brainwashed. Kari, how can you let him go so easily?'

'It's not easy.' Her eyes flashed. 'Don't think any of this is easy for me. It's not.'

'You and he would have been married by now,' Barbara pointed out sadly.

'I guess,' Kari said, and the hurt was still there in her eyes. 'You know something? I've never had to face losing anything that mattered to me before. If I've learned anything from all of this, it's that you can't change people or make them do what you want. And if you truly love them, then that's the last thing you should ever want to do.'

Michael made to protest, but saw the simple truth in Kari's words. Wasn't he guilty of doing such a thing himself? Hadn't he tried to force Mike to toe the line by making life as difficult as possible for him?

'From what I gather,' Kari went on, 'Amy's father is a real regular guy, happy to go along with things the way they are. But Mike came on the scene and talked him into making changes at the farm. Changes which involved borrowing heavily to improve the farm and buying in more livestock. I don't know if I'm right, but I think that's how this foot and mouth thing got into the herd — through the new cattle.'

'So you're saying it's all Mike's fault, what's happened?' Barbara asked, horrified.

'No. Not exactly. But it was Mike who convinced Mr Palmer that to make the farm viable for the future, he had to expand. The place would have died on its feet without the improvements. If it hadn't been for this tragic outbreak of foot and mouth, that farm would have thrived. It could have become a real little goldmine. Mike's a good businessman, Dad.' Unconsciously she slipped into calling him Dad, but no one seemed to notice. 'He wouldn't have got the Palmers into something that wasn't economically sound, we both know that. It wasn't Mike's fault that fate made things go so tragically wrong. It wasn't his fault that Jed Palmer wasn't insured either.'

'I don't understand why you're telling us all this, Kari,' Barbara said.

She glanced at her husband and saw he was too stunned to utter a word.

'Like I said, I've been thinking.' Kari smiled thinly. 'There must be some way all of us can get Mike and the Palmers out of this financial mess.'

'What?' Michael spluttered.

'We need to find out how much it would take to get that farm back on its feet. And once that part of it is resolved, Mike and Amy will be free to sort out their differences and get back together. Look, folks, I'm telling you they belong together. No one knows Mike better than I do. I know he'll never be happy unless he's with the girl he loves. And . . . ' She tilted her head high as she spoke. 'That girl is Amy Carter.'

'Kari,' Michael said slowly, 'you're one heck of a girl, do you know that?'

Kari gave a little smile and Barbara couldn't help noticing a change in the girl she'd known all her life. The sometimes over-confident air she'd always exuded before had disappeared. There was a softer, more feminine side to her now, Barbara noted, and it suited her. Then she caught on to Michael's conversation and any further speculation ended abruptly.

'I could free Mike's own funds, I suppose,' he mused, 'and make the capital available for whatever needs to be done. But you're forgetting one very important thing, Kari. Farming folk are proud, independent people. I don't suppose they're any different here to the way they are the world over. What makes you think the Palmers will accept my offer of help?'

Kari's face fell.

'I'm not shooting your idea down in flames, honey,' he said. 'But we really can't go much further until I've met with the Palmers and sounded them out. Why don't you leave it with me meantime? I'll sort something out.' He fell silent and rubbed his hands wearily across tired, red eyes. 'Before I do anything else,' he said grimly, 'I've got to see Mike and thrash things out with him.'

'You won't be too hard on him, will you?' Barbara pleaded anxiously. 'In fact, why don't you let me talk to him first, dear?'

'No. I have to talk to him man to man. You can pick up the pieces when I've finished with him.'

Barbara went pale.

⋆ ⋆ ⋆

Michael hesitated outside the run-down cottage. It was obviously undergoing fairly extensive renovations, but was still a far cry from the lifestyle Mike was used to back home. How could he want to give everything up for this down-market little place? He turned, looked at the view and shrugged. No better than the view from their chalet in the Colorado mountains in any spring. Or the outlook from their house in New England in the fall. No, there was nothing here Mike couldn't have at home — except this girl. Amy.

At the front door, he raised his hand

to knock, then changed his mind and pushed it open. Mike spun round when he heard the door open.

'Dad!' he cried, his pleasure at seeing his father obvious in the warmth of his smile. He held out his hand, then saw his father's dark expression and let it drop limply at his side. The last thing he wanted or needed right now was a bitter confrontation with someone else he loved.

The anger that had been boiling inside the older Carter for so long was reduced to a simmer. There had been so much that he had wanted to say . . . The shabby treatment Mike had meted out to Kari, the way he had thrown everything back in his father's face . . . it all faded into insignificance now.

Mike looked tanned and fit, but there was a sadness in his eyes that made his father look away.

'It's good to see you, Dad,' Mike said. 'But if you've come for an argument, I don't think I can face that right now.'

'I don't want to argue with you, Mike.' Michael spoke softly. He longed to reach out and hug his son, but he checked himself. 'There were a lot of things I wanted to say to you, but now I'm here, I guess there's only one question I want to ask you — and your answer is mighty important. So I'd appreciate it if you'd be straight with me, son.'

'Fire away,' Mike said defiantly. 'I won't lie to you, Dad. You know that much.'

'This English girl,' Michael said. 'Amy. Do you really love her? It's not just a physical thing?'

Mike stood motionless. At length he spoke, looking directly at his father. 'Dad, after all I've been through since coming here, there's no doubt in my mind that I love Amy. It's because of me her whole life's messed up now, and she'd be perfectly justified in hating me.' He broke off. 'But I don't reckon she does, however it might appear.'

'OK, that's all I needed to know,'

Michael said firmly. 'I've heard all about the foot and mouth outbreak and I also know that you can't be held responsible. Just remember this, Mike. No problem, however big, is ever insurmountable.'

'Maybe not for you, Dad, with all your money,' Mike said evenly. 'But the Palmers have lost everything.'

'I know. But I've an idea that might help them and I'd like to know what you think.' He looked steadily at his son. 'Say I release your funds, then you buy the Palmers out of this mess?'

Mike shrugged hopelessly. 'Even if you did that, I wouldn't have enough cash to cover it,' he admitted. 'I don't think you realise just how deeply in debt Amy's folks are.'

'Well, obviously, I'd throw in a few bucks.' Michael sighed with exasperation. 'Call it a wedding present — supposing you get back together.' He beamed expansively. 'But we still have to talk to the Palmers and hear what they think.'

Mike dared to look hopeful. It all sounded so easy and, from the way he was talking, his shrewd father had obviously been thinking it all through, weighing everything up.

'You know, son, all your mom and I want — all we've ever wanted — is your happiness. And if your future is really here, as you say . . . ' He paused for a moment, glanced round the basic cottage and sighed. 'We'll back you to the hilt.'

'Thanks, Dad.' Mike looked relieved. 'You don't know how much it means to me to hear you say that. As for your plan for the farm, I think it sounds just terrific. It wouldn't cost you a fortune either. All the Palmers really need is some capital to keep them afloat and to restock the herd.'

The two men stared at each other for a moment, then Michael stepped forward and embraced his son.

'I've missed you, Dad,' Mike said huskily.

'Me too, son. More than you'll ever

know,' he said, slapping Mike on the back.

They laughed, partly embarrassed by this sudden outward show of affection, partly relieved that the rift between them was, at last, healed.

'This is the best idea you've had, Dad,' Mike said.

'That's just where you're wrong, Mike. It's not my idea. It's Kari's. All I can say is, I hope that this Amy is half the girl Kari is. But if you're sure you've made the right choice, then remember you're a Carter and get out there and fight for what you want!'

★  ★  ★

The farmhouse kitchen had never seen so many people. The gathering had started in the sitting-room, but everyone gravitated towards the homely kitchen. Jed looked around, hardly able to believe that his fortunes had undergone so many changes in the past few weeks. Just when he thought that he'd hit rock bottom, along had come Michael Carter with his plan of action.

This big-hearted American wanted to buy into the farm, despite the dire straits it was in, on behalf of his son. Jed looked across at Mike and raised his glass to him. To Mike Carter Junior, who was now his partner.

They were holding this party to celebrate the signing of the contracts, and virtually everyone he knew from around these parts was here — even Sam and Kate Threadwell, who were arguing good-naturedly in the corner. He looked around the sea of happy, smiling faces and caught a glimpse of Amy.

She alone was unsmiling. Her face was still wan, and the light had gone from her eyes. He'd do anything to see his daughter smile again — anything. But it was out of his hands — something that she alone could resolve.

'Come on, Jed,' Sheila hissed in his ear. 'I know you're all pleased with yourself now that everything's sorted out, but could you maybe circulate a bit?' She smiled as Michael held out his glass to be refilled with the champagne he'd brought to the party. He thanked her and turned speak to his son.

'I thought you were crazy, wanting to stay here,' he said, grinning widely. 'But now I'm beginning to see why. It sure is a beautiful part of the world, the people are great, and Amy there — she's a real stunner. Is she always as quiet as this, though?' He looked troubled for a moment, then continued. 'I've sure as heck never seen you looking so good, Mike. The outdoor life obviously agrees with you. Maybe you've some of the pioneering spirit of the early settlers in you after all.'

Mike wished he could feel as happy as everyone else, but the truth was he'd hardly exchanged two words with Amy since their break-up and he feared they'd never get together again.

'Mind you, I guess I wouldn't really be happy living here in such peace and solitude.' Michael Senior laughed. 'I need the hustle and bustle of the city.'

Mike laughed then, realising, too, that his father would never be able to settle for the simple life. He looked across for Amy and caught sight of her just as she was slipping out of the kitchen.

Barbara stood chatting warmly to Sheila. She'd felt a sense of ease between them from the very first moment they'd met. 'You've taken good care of Mike these past weeks, Sheila,' she said happily. 'I've never seen him look so healthy, or so happy.'

'He's had nothing he didn't deserve,' Sheila said with a smile. 'I just treat him like one of my own, Barbara. You must be very proud of him. And I'll never forget that Jed owes him his life.'

Barbara smiled. 'He's a good boy, but I wouldn't be happy about being so far from him if I didn't know he was here with you and your family. And Amy's a lovely girl. Where is she, by the way? I haven't seen her for a while.'

Sheila looked around for her elder

daughter, her eyes troubled. 'Oh, she'll be somewhere about.'

* * *

Amy was outside. The sun had disappeared, leaving the sky striped with grey and amber and red. Soon there would be cows in the yard again, and her father would have a purpose to his life. She should be feeling buoyant again, but her spirits refused to lift.

She moved across the yard to the little garden at the side of the house that her mother tended. She leaned on the wall, watching the sunset over the mountains, dark in the fading light.

She'd do anything to take back those bitter words she'd thrown at Mike, anything to erase the memory of the pain in his eyes as she'd wrenched off her engagement ring and flung it on the table in front of him.

She turned abruptly and saw Mike leaning against the house, watching her. Her heart turned over at the sight of him, so tall, so lean and strong. She turned away quickly in case she gave her feelings away. She loved him so much, but how could she ever take back the cruel things she'd said? She trembled at the memory.

'I came out for some air,' he said, walking over to her to stand so close that she could smell the faint musky tang of his aftershave. She felt as if her heart were in her throat, stifling her breathing.

'Yes,' she said stiffly. 'It's hot in there. All those people.'

'Noisy, too.'

'Yes.'

They were silent for a moment, then both made to speak at once.

'You first,' he said with a gentle smile.

She looked up at him. Even in the gathering darkness, his eyes were soft and full of love for her.

'I was just going to say, all this, getting things sorted out with the farm, has happened so fast. It's kind of like the way it was for us.' She caught her breath, half-wishing she hadn't said anything.

'I know what you mean.' Absently, he reached out and began to play with a strand of her hair, letting it fall through his fingers. 'Nothing's changed,' he said softly. 'As far as I'm concerned, anyway. I know exactly how I feel inside. I love you, Amy. I thought I did the first moment I saw you, but compared with the way I feel now, that was nothing . . . I know one thing, though. From that very first time I saw you, I've been sure that you are the only girl for me. Amy, I love you so much.'

She looked up at him, eyes brimming with tears that spilled unchecked on to her cheeks. They stood, only inches between them, before Amy threw herself into his arms. 'Oh, Mike, it's the same for me! Without you, these past few days have been a nightmare. I love you, too, and I can't live without you.'

Mike tightened his arms around her, drawing her close, smelling the sweet scent of her hair. Then at last his lips touched hers and his senses were spiralling.

The side door of the farmhouse opened a shade, then closed again; and through the dizzying haze of love, Mike felt a tugging sensation at his feet. He looked down briefly and saw that Cosby had joined them, eager to butt in, growling as he chewed up yet another pair of shoelaces.

Laughing ecstatically, Mike hugged Amy tightly. Nothing would ever come between them again — he wouldn't let it. He reached down for her hand, then gently, slowly, looking into her eyes, he slipped her engagement ring back on her finger. Raising her hand to his lips, he kissed the ring, then her hand.

'I love you, Amy,' he murmured. 'Marry me?'

'Oh, yes, Mike, yes,' she breathed as he gathered her to him and kissed her over and over again.

\* \* \*

The roar of aircraft taking to the skies, or landing; people talking; flight announcements being made — all contributed to the general buzz of activity at the airport. The senior Carters had gone off to find a cup of coffee before their flight was called. They disappeared among the crowds of people, with Michael still protesting that he'd prefer a double Scotch and Barbara still insisting on coffee.

Mike lost sight of them, then turned to look at his companions: Kari, beautiful and sophisticated as ever; and his fiancée, Amy, so gentle and loving. His eyes held hers for a moment before he turned to Kari.

'Mike, while you're saying goodbye to Kari,' Amy said softly, 'I'm going to buy myself a magazine.'

'Don't be long,' he said, catching her hand briefly before she turned away. She looked over her shoulder as she walked off and smiled confidently and he felt his heart flip over inside him. Would it always be like this? he wondered.

Right now, though, he was grateful to Amy for being so understanding. Taking

Kari's arm, he led her off to a quiet corner, away from the hustle and bustle of the airport lounge.

'I've wanted to talk to you,' he said earnestly. 'But there just hasn't been a chance over the last few days. So much has happened. But what I do know, Kari, is that it's all down to you. I don't know how to thank you for all you've done for the Palmers and for me. All that happened between us in the past . . . I want you to know I'll never forget that.'

Kari gave a wry smile.

'I still care about you, you know,' he said gruffly. 'I guess I always will, Kari, but . . . '

'I know.' She smiled. 'It's OK, Mike. Really. You don't have to spell it out for me. I love you, too — in the same way. Like a friend, a dear friend. I'm glad I realised that in time before I let jealousy destroy even that.'

'You're amazing,' he said, cuffing her gently under the chin. 'And, Kari, I'll never be able to forget that I found my happiness at your expense.'

Kari suppressed a rueful smile. He was wearing that irresistible little-boy-lost look. Poor Mike. He'd be haunted by the fact he'd run out on her all his life if she let him. The Kari who'd come to England to win him back would have enjoyed that, would have delighted in his discomfort, but this Kari didn't.

'Your happiness has always been important to me, Mike,' she said softly. 'But believe me, it sure wasn't easy to throw in the towel and admit I'd lost.' She broke off and this time the smile on her face was wistful. 'If you can find happiness and true love, maybe one day I'll find that kind of happiness for myself, too.'

Mike nodded and looked beyond Kari to the guy sitting quietly at the end of a row of seats. Even sitting there, he was attracting quite a few admiring glances from girls and women alike that passed, but he had eyes only for one young woman. He was deep in thought, staring at Kari; but as she, following

Mike's gaze, turned and looked, he smiled and waved. She waved back and Mike was pretty sure Kari blushed.

Phil Scott had obviously been watching Kari all the time, never taking his eyes off her.

'Maybe that happiness we were talking about isn't too far away for you either, Kari,' Mike said softly.

She turned back to Mike, smiling teasingly, the blush still lingering on her cheeks. 'Maybe,' she said simply.

As they spoke, Mike thought she had the look of a woman who was loved — calm and confident. Maybe even the look of a woman in love.

Mike looked up and saw Amy threading her way through the crowds towards him and his heart soared at the very sight of her. He knew, without a doubt, that he would never tire of looking at her, or of loving her.

This may have started as love at first sight, but it had mellowed into something quite different.

This was real, and this was for ever.

We do hope that you have enjoyed reading this large print book.

Did you know that all of our titles are available for purchase?

We publish a wide range of high quality large print books including:
**Romances, Mysteries, Classics**
**General Fiction**
**Non Fiction and Westerns**

Special interest titles available in large print are:
**The Little Oxford Dictionary**
**Music Book, Song Book**
**Hymn Book, Service Book**

Also available from us courtesy of Oxford University Press:
**Young Readers' Dictionary**
**(large print edition)**
**Young Readers' Thesaurus**
**(large print edition)**

For further information or a free brochure, please contact us at:
**Ulverscroft Large Print Books Ltd.,**
**The Green, Bradgate Road, Anstey,**
**Leicester, LE7 7FU, England.**
**Tel:** (00 44) **0116 236 4325**
**Fax:** (00 44) **0116 234 0205**

# FORGOTTEN

## Fay Cunningham

Driving home in the dark, Serena stops to help an injured man lying in a ditch. He mutters something unintelligible, but that is only the start of her problems. Someone is watching the apartment she shares with her brother, her mother is being particularly secretive, and police detective Jack Armstrong is convinced Serena is hiding something. Just when she thinks things can get no worse, her missing father turns up. This is definitely not the time to fall in love.

# A PERFECT RHAPSODY

## Dawn Bridge

After an unhappy romance with a concert pianist, Emma joins her local orchestra — something she has always wanted to do. Their new young conductor, Paul, seems to be an aloof and arrogant man, but Emma finds herself attracted to him. What secret is he concealing? Will she be able to break through the barrier which he has erected around himself? And how can she ever hope to compete with the beautiful Samantha for his affections, whilst dealing with admirers of her own?

# TIDES OF LOVE

## Phyllis Mallett

When her widowed father dies, Clarissa Marston is left penniless. George Farand, however, has a solution: in debt to the late Mr. Marston, he invites Clarissa to stay with his family at their Cornish estate of Trevarron until he can repay her the money. She warms to the genial John Farand, despite his darkly brooding brother Edwin. But Trevarron is a place of ominous secrets, and Clarissa begins to fear for her safety — until the handsome Richard Redmond comes to her aid . . .

# FATE IN FREEFALL

## Ken Preston

Paralysed by grief after losing her fiancé in a skydiving accident, Katrina Maslow cannot allow herself to love another man. She travels the world in an attempt to flee from her former life, ending up in Rio and accepting a job as a guide with J Stone Adventure Trips. But Jay, the handsome owner of the company, is determined to break down her reserves. As they are pursued by a ruthless killer, Katrina finally realises she is in love with Jay — just at the moment she might lose him forever . . .

# THE TIGER IN MEN

## Denise Robins

When Fenella Shaw left England to take possession of a Canadian cattle ranch in the Saskatchewan Valley, gifted to her as a legacy by her father, she quickly fell in love with handsome Max Geerling, the manager. It came as no surprise to anyone when the news of their engagement was announced, the neighbouring farmers believing them to be ideally matched. But Max is not all he seems to be — and Fenella finds herself caught up in a situation so alien to her that she fears she may never escape . . .